HISTORY ENHANCED

SHORT STORIES

GEORGE THOMAS CLARK

Published by George Thomas Clark
ISBN: 979-8-9914942-0-5 – Trade Paperback
Bakersfield, California
webmaster@GeorgeThomasClark.com

Books by
George Thomas Clark

Hitler Here
The Bold Investor
Paint it Blue
They Make Movies
Autobiography of George Thomas Clark
Where Will We Sleep?
Basketball and Football
Death in the Ring
Down Goes Trump
King Donald
Obama on Edge
Echoes from Saddam Hussein
Political Satire for Progressives
Tales of Romance
In Other Hands
Anne Frank on Tour and Other Stories
History Enhanced

Acknowledgments

Since this book is based on history, I am delighted to thank those whose works were particularly important in establishing what is known.

The brilliant but tragic actor Robert Walker would be less understood today if not for the research and insight of Beverly Linet, who authored *Star-Crossed: The Story of Robert Walker and Jennifer Jones*. Joan Bennett and her father and sister Constance were beautiful stars of stage and screen but suffered from a variety of difficulties chronicled in *The Bennetts: An Acting Family* by Brian Kellow.

Bakersfield.com and local television network affiliates for several years filed timely reports and videos about the investigation of Vincent Brothers and his trial for a nightmarish crime. Michelle McNamara devoted much time and passion, and ultimately her life, to writing *I'll Be Gone in the Dark* about Joe DeAngelo, a then-unidentified man who first terrorized Central California and then Southern California.

Senator Joseph McCarthy, the fanatical hunter of communists, is brought into focus by Haynes Johnson in *The Age of Anxiety, McCarthyism to Terrorism*. Richard and Pat Nixon are portrayed in a personal way by daughter Julie Nixon-Eisenhower in her book *Pat Nixon: The Untold Story*. Fidel Castro is recalled by many, who include Nikita Khrushchev in *Khrushchev Remembers* and David Halberstam in *The Best and the Brightest*.

Introduction

History Enhanced offers part of the official record, and the author's creative writing and insights help us understand much of what else could have happened in seven penetrating short stories.

Robert Walker – Walker, a talented actor but shy and nervous young man, marries beautiful and gifted actress Jennifer Jones and believes he has found eternal happiness. Instead, legendary producer David O. Selznick pursues his wife while Walker descends into mental illness.

Power Couple – Few actresses in Hollywood history have been as beautiful as Joan Bennett, who is also a fine actress. Men pursue her, and she always needs a man, but her marriage to prominent producer Walter Wanger leads to unforeseeable problems.

The Educator – Vincent Brothers, a prominent vice principal, is respected on campus but sometimes violent at home. In this story readers witness the mounting turmoil in his private life with girlfriends, wives, children, and his mother-in-law.

Alternative Interrogation – Joe DeAngelo is accused of being a serial rapist and murderer. In this imaginative story, a mysterious investigator gets tough with the suspect, demanding the truth.

The Slugger – Senator Joseph McCarthy portrays himself as the most patriotic man in America while he pursues communists real and imagined. In reality, he's a depressed alcoholic and his most dangerous enemy.

Nixon Responds – Young Richard Nixon is bright and talented but resentful about a myriad of people he believes have wronged him. He marries a lovely and supportive woman, Pat, who helps his political career. But, as readers watch, he battles her and colleagues as well as enemies as his inner turmoil grows.

Fidel Forever – Fidel thinks he has charisma and special political talent, and he does. He also believes he can destroy or at least thwart political adversaries anywhere in the world. Sometimes he's right but, as he slides into megalomania, his personal and professional relationships suffer.

Contents

HOLLYWOOD HEARTACHE

Robert Walker

Bob's not a bad kid. He just feels sad and nervous a lot and gets poor grades and tells his teachers they're boring and teases and squeezes girls till they cry and he loses fights to bigger boys but behaves for a child psychiatrist who tells his reserved parents, "Someday, I think Robert will be fine."

He doesn't want to worry about that and runs away when he's thirteen but before long, hungry and dirty, he returns home and his parents send him from the family in Ogden, Utah to a military school near San Diego.

He hates classes there, too, and is still weaker than most boys but they're friendlier when he takes a music class and practices hard to become lead drummer in the band. Following a concert, the music teacher's wife approaches and says, "Robert, you have stage presence. I want you to read for a part in our next play."

"I'd like to, Mrs. Davis, but I don't have any acting experience."

"Don't worry," she says. "We'll start with a minor part."

Bob's scared before the performance but loses himself in the character and senses the audience enjoys his work and soon, in a larger role, is thrilled but not surprised he wins first place for best actor in the region, and he stars in several plays he considers more important than academics. In his senior year history teacher Mr. Walsh walks to his desk and says, "Robert, please stay a few minutes after class so we can talk."

"Sure," says Bob. "Everything all right?"

Mr. Walsh doesn't reply. He waits until the other students leave and returns and points at the textbook on Bob's desk. "Young man, you're going to have to be more diligent. You memorize your lines in all those plays, so I know you could remember history assignments if you did the reading. Other teachers have similar concerns."

He can't do his homework. He's busy showing people a written scholarship offer from the distinguished Pasadena Playhouse.

"They want me to start in the fall," he tells the school superinten-dent, Mr. Flagler.

"That's very impressive, Robert, but you'll have to graduate first, and you're simply not going to make it this year, as we've so often informed you. Apply yourself here for another year. Next spring you'll still only be eighteen and will have plenty of time for a career in theater."

Bob writes to the Pasadena Playhouse, explaining his predicament, and receives this reply: "That's fine, Mr. Walker. We'll reserve your scholarship for next year."

It's painful sitting in classes he'd failed last year, but he thinks about applause in Pasadena and does enough homework to pass.

In a long letter to his wealthy Aunt Tenny, who lives in New York, he discusses his acting ambition and asks for advice, and she responds, "The Pasadena Playhouse is marvelous, Robert, but Broadway is the theatrical capital of the world, and you really should come here to study at the American Academy of Dramatic Arts. I would be delighted to pay for your tuition and provide an allowance."

"Thanks so much, Aunt Tenny," he writes back.

Bob lives with his brother Walt near the academy in New York and starts studying drama and diction and even dancing and fencing and thinks he's doing all right but not like the dark-haired beauty everyone notices but who he's sure never sees him pass in the halls.

"Who's that stunning young lady?" he asks a male student.

"Phylis Isley," he says. "She played a lot of summer stock in her family's company."

"It shows."

Bob watches Phylis practice parts with other students in the academy's theater and knows half the guys here must be in love with her and tells himself he's not good enough. She'd prefer someone handsomer and more relaxed. He wishes he had nerves like most people who feel good and live normally. He doesn't think he can, unless Phylis someday wants to marry him.

He has to try. It's been four months. He can't wait any longer. This afternoon he's going to talk to her. He walks into the theater and sees her playing the wife of some tall blond guy, and she's wonderful. He wants them to keep acting so he can enjoy her work and won't have to introduce himself. He considers waiting another week but knows that would be painful. Besides, they're finishing. The blond student says bye and Phylis gathers her coat and script then walks toward the door where he's standing.

"Oh, excuse me," Bob says.

She stops and smiles, and he tries to smile back and says, "You're a wonderful actress, and I hope we can practice sometime."

"I'd love to," she says. "I'm Phylis Isley."

"Robert Walker."

"Yes, I know."

"You're kidding."

She laughs and says, "Not at all. People tell me you're a fine actor."

Robert and Phylis are soon daily practicing scenes from Shakespeare to the present, and they're getting better fast and enjoying an adventure he prays lasts forever. He knows it might not, though. He worries that he can't support Phylis. She probably expects a lot. Her father's a prominent film distributor and theater owner. And she's too alluring not to succeed. Bob, on the other hand, knows he's cute but not a leading man. He's the other guy or younger brother and might not earn much in acting.

Still, they love taking walks in Central Park and going to movies and plays they analyze afterward, and at the academy they enjoy working on their auditions for the second and final year of the program.

"I guarantee you'll be invited back, Phyl," he says.

"You, too."

"You think so?"

"I certainly do."

She's right. The American Academy of Dramatic Arts wants both to return in the fall. This summer Phyl is touring the Midwest with her father's theatrical troupe, and Bob's unhappy hustling to find a job and going home alone and thinking about his girlfriend acting in plays with good looking young men and meeting prominent people in every town and he wonders if she'll still like him or even return to New York. He can't sleep. He can't eat. He doesn't care about acting.

"Come on, Bob, settle down," says Walt. "You're making far too much of this. She'll be back in the fall. Go get a job to take your mind off her."

He needs to escape hot and lonely New York and, after rejections for menial labor in the city, he goes to the docks and gets a job moving cargo on a transport ship that sails to steamy Central America. He writes Phyl what he's doing and implies he might not return to the academy.

"I'm stunned and hurt by your selfish decision," she responds. "Were you not going to discuss this with me? You could have waited until my return. We'll personally talk about this in three weeks. I hope…"

Bob concludes he's incredibly stupid and longs to see her and quits his job and sails back to New York. His brother Walt is disgusted and tells him, "Go find your own place to live. And grow up," and Aunt Tenny says, "You're an ingrate and will receive no further assistance from me." He's lucky to rent a tiny apartment at the YMCA which pays him fifty cents a day to mow the lawn and wash dishes and help keep the place clean.

On a hot afternoon later that week he showers and shaves with extra care because Phyl will soon arrive by train. He's nervous but ecstatic when she appears at the station, and he runs to hug and kiss her and notes with relief that she's elated to see him. They go to the dormitory for young ladies and Phyl checks in and unpacks upstairs while Bob waits in the lobby, as required, and in a little while they hold hands on a walk.

"Do you really want to quit the academy?" she asks.

"I don't know why I feel that way. Maybe it's because you were gone."

"If you're not returning, I'm not, either. We'll start our acting careers together."

Bob embraces her and never wants to let go.

5

"I'll call my parents tomorrow," she says.

Phillip and Flora Mae Isley are stunned and rush from their Tulsa home to New York and check into a beautiful hotel and invite the young couple to dinner.

"Phyl, this is a mistake," says her father. "You've always been such a sensible girl."

"I've been acting all my life and know I'm ready."

"She's going to be the biggest star in the world," Bob assures them.

"Do you have any opportunities, Phyl?" asks her mother.

"Not at present, but Bob and I will be looking for roles every day."

"Young man," says Mr. Isley, "I'm worried about your professional prospects."

"He's a wonderful actor, Dad," says Phyl.

"I don't doubt it," he says, "but I understand the difficulties for a young man trying to make it as an actor. As you know, I thought I'd be the next Barrymore, but a streak of rejections and my marriage to your mother, and then your birth, compelled me to abandon theater and move into the business side of acting."

"I know we'll get some roles soon," Bob says.

"We shall see," Mrs. Isley says.

A few weeks later Phyl tells Bob, "My father's gotten me a good radio show in Tulsa. Twenty-five dollars a week."

Bob's stomach drops, and he says, "Oh, congratulations. When do you leave?"

"I don't know that I'm going anywhere. I told my father and the radio station that I won't take the job unless they offer you a good role at the same salary."

In a few days Phyl and Bob are accepted and a week later get on a bus with their few belongings and move to Tulsa. She lives with her parents in their elegant home and he rents a small room in the city.

"Join us for dinner tonight," Phyl says on the phone.

"I'm embarrassed eating there almost every night."

"My parents know I won't be here unless you are."

"I hope they like me," he says.

"I think they do, but every day they tell me I'm too young to marry anyone. I'll be relieved when our radio contract ends in December."

"You know what January second is, don't you, Phyl?" Bob asks.

She takes his hands and says, "The first anniversary of the day we met."

He breathes deeply and exhales. "And on that special day, I hope you'll marry me."

"Yes, yes, yes. I can't wait…"

They marry in a small private ceremony and that evening check into a Tulsa hotel suite and instantly start kissing and this time they don't have to stop. Bob's not sure what to do but is thrilled when Phyl starts undressing and he does the same and they roll onto the bed and caress each other in an enchanting new world.

In the morning Mr. and Mrs. Isley meet them at the hotel for breakfast, and he says, "Bob, Phyl told me neither of you want any support, and that's commendable, but Mrs. Isley and I insist you accept a very practical wedding present. Shall we take a look?"

They walk outside and see an ornate 1939 Packard convertible parked in front, and Phyl says, "Thanks so much, Mom and Dad."

"That's an incredible gift, Mr. and Mrs. Isley."

"The first place you should drive is to Hollywood," he says. "I have contacts there and you can pursue your dreams. Here's a letter of introduction."

Shortly after Bob and Phyl arrive in the warm and exotic movie capital, Paramount offers them a chance to select the material and audition together and they perform challenging scenes.

"I would've preferred something lighter that appeals to larger audiences," says the studio chief, "but we may have something for you in a little while."

Paramount never responds.

In a few weeks Bob and Phyl can't find anything but bit parts and he tells his her, "It's time to take your dad's letter of introduction to his friend at Republic Pictures."

"I'm not working for that junk factory."

"Give it a try."

A week later he drives their Packard to the modest Republic studio and drops off Phyl in the morning, and that afternoon he retrieves an actress who just signed a six-month contract for seventy-five dollars a week.

"That's wonderful," Bob says, leaning over for a kiss. "You'll soon be the brightest star in Hollywood."

She smiles but shakes her head. "At least they've got a small role for me in *New Frontier*. We start shooting in three days."

"What's it about?"

"Cowboys and horses. That's all they make."

They finish shooting the fifty-minute movie in less than a week.

"Besides you, did they have anyone with talent?"

"Very few," she says. "But their biggest cowboy, John Wayne, is a handsome man."

Phyl then takes fourth billing in a fifteen-part Dick Tracy serial while Bob drives around, worrying he'll be rejected at the next studio and feeling bad when that happens.

A week later, her few scenes complete, she says, "I didn't have more than twenty words in the whole thing. I can't endure this, Bob. The screenplays are bad and everyone's in a hurry to churn out a product. I've got to get out of this contract so we can return to New York."

Mr. Isley helps Phyl end a deal Republic Pictures didn't care about anyway and she and Bob sell their Packard for a thousand dollars and take the train across the nation and rent a thimble of an apartment in Manhattan. They think they're ready for a breakthrough but they're a month late for most auditions and told to wait and one morning Bob says, "Phyl, you've hardly eaten anything the last few days. Maybe we should take you to the doctor."

"Yes, we'd better."

The doctor examines her and declares, "Young lady, you're pregnant."

When Phyl steps into the doctor's office and tells Bob, he embraces and kisses her and says, "That's wonderful," but soon remembers she won't be able to work, and he doesn't have any roles as their expenses are about to soar. While Phyl stays home, Robert searches and finds some roles in radio, and in April 1940 they welcome Robert Walker Jr.

"He looks like his papa," says Phyl.

"I hope that's a compliment."

"It certainly is."

Bob's popular radio performances generate more work and in a few months the family moves to a modest house an hour from town.

"Don't forget," she says, "I'll be striding the boards of Broadway as soon as Bobby's a little larger."

He hustles to radio dramas many mornings, afternoons, and evenings, and his salary jumps again, and they advance to a nicer home nearby.

"Say, Phyl, can you help me with my lines for the show tomorrow?"

"Of course."

"We'll soon be doing this with your scripts," he says.

"I don't see how. I'm a full-time nanny, changing diapers and performing a thousand other errands."

"You'll be on top before we know it."

Phyl frequently seems sad and listless and often looks out the window. Bob worries she's alone too much and resolves to spend as much time with her as he can.

"I know I can still act, Bob. If I had a job, I could act better than ever."

"I tell everyone you're ready for great roles. Here, let's work on some of these scripts."

In little more than a week he sees his wife crying, and from behind he massages her shoulders and asks, "What's wrong?"

"It's happening again."

"What?"

"I think I'm pregnant."

"That's wonderful."

"For you, maybe so."

Phyl gives birth to Michael in March 1941. She soon recovers and three times they see *Claudia*, the best play on Broadway this season.

"I must play that part, Bob," she says after each performance. "Every young actress wants it."

Less than a month later, he asks, "Did you hear? David O. Selznick just paid almost two hundred thousand dollars for the movie rights."

"I certainly did. I'd love to be Claudia on screen, too."

Bob asks his agent to try to help her, and he arranges for Phyl and another ingenue to meet the play's author, Rose Franken, and rehearse for several days at her farm in Old Lyme, Connecticut. On her last night there, Phyl calls and excitedly says, "Bob, Rose told David O. Selznick about me, and he wants me to read for Katharine Brown. She's head of his New York office."

"We'll start rehearsing soon as you get home."

Phyl works with Bob and several other actors for a month and is primed for her July audition. He feels how nervous she is before driving into the city this morning and worries about her until she returns late in the afternoon.

"What happened?"

"I was horrible," she says.

"I can't imagine that. What did Katharine Brown say?"

"I ran out in tears before she could tell me how bad I was."

"Don't worry, Phyl. A little while before you arrived, Mrs. Brown's secretary called and asked you to come in tomorrow afternoon."

"I don't need to be rejected in person."

"I bet Mrs. Brown wants to give you another chance. You should go."

He leaves early the next morning for a radio program and that evening is anxious to ask, "How'd the reading turn out?"

"I got to meet David O. Selznick. Imagine, the man who made *Gone with the Wind*."

"What did he think?"

"Mr. Selznick didn't want me to read. He preferred to talk and learn about my life. I told him about you and the kids and my ambition. He likes me, Bob, and he believes in my potential as an actress."

Bob keeps playing good roles in radio, and Phyl signs a personal contract with Selznick's production company for two hundred dollars weekly for a year.

"That's wonderful," he says, "except you'll be in Los Angeles."

"Only for a month. Mr. Selznick wants me to star in a play in Santa Barbara and then take several screen tests."

When she's away, Phyl and Bob talk by phone every night, and he often tells her, "The boys and I miss you terribly."

"I miss all of you just as much."

"I'll have a surprise when you get home."

"What?"

"Our new home in beautiful Sands Point."

"I've also got something new. Mr. Selznick has renamed me Jennifer Jones."

"You'll always be Phyl to me."

"He thinks the public will better remember this name."

"What happened to your role in *Claudia*?" he asks.

"Mr. Selznick sold his rights to the property."

"So, what role does he have for you and when do you start?"

"He's looking for the right story and promises he'll find it."

Finally, Phyl returns and loves their home where they play with the boys and walk on the beach, and he'd never imagined being so happy.

On a serene summer day in 1942 the phone rings and Bob answers.

"This is David O. Selznick. May I please speak to Jennifer?"

"You mean, Phylis."

"No, Jennifer has immersed herself in the new name and is quite comfortable with it. Is she there?"

"Let me check," Bob says, and walks into the living room where Jennifer is reading. "It's Mr. Selznick. Do you want to talk to him?"

"Of course," she says, tossing her book on the coffee table and running into the kitchen.

Bob quietly moves into the living room and hears her say, "I'm honored you want to discuss my career, Mr. Selznick. I'm free any time. Tomorrow night at six. Oh, that's my favorite restaurant. See you then."

Bob returns to the kitchen and Phyl says, "This is the opportunity I've always worked for."

"Did he invite me, too?"

"Just business this time."

Bob plays with the kids that night and puts them to bed. After ten Phyl returns and hugs him, announcing, "Mr. Selznick says he's going to make sure the whole world falls in love with me, like he did for Ingrid Bergman and Joan Fontaine. He's also giving me a new seven-year contract."

"He's a powerful man who knows how to promote talented people, especially beautiful women like my wife."

A few weeks later the phone rings and Bob answers.

"This is David O. Selznick. May I please speak to Jennifer?"

"Sure, Mr. Selznick. I'll get her."

Phyl walks to their phone in the kitchen and from the living room Bob hears her say, "That's wonderful, Mr. Selznick. I'd love to audition. I've heard so much about *The Song of Bernadette*. Yes, please do send me the book. I'll read it on the train to Hollywood. See you in two weeks."

Bob walks to Phyl and says, "The part's as good as yours."

"Not yet. Twentieth Century-Fox will decide."

"Mr. Selznick can help. His brother-in-law's a top executive there."

"I'm going to earn it with my performance."

When Phyl leaves that fall Bob dreads not seeing her for three months he needs to finish his radio obligations and sell the house and prepare to move two kids three thousand miles. He worries about her every night but at least Selznick productions is providing a safe apartment for her in Beverly Hills.

Every time the phone rings, Bob prays it's Phyl. If it isn't, he calls her.

"I'm pretty blue without you," he says. "I assume Mr. Selznick plans to introduce you to all the stars and producers."

"I wish he would. It feels like he's hiding me."

"Tell him."

"I did, but he explained that my screen tests present a saintly woman, and I shouldn't let the public see me in mundane places around town."

Bob cares for the kids and commutes to New York several days a week to record his radio shows and yearns to talk to Phyl, the best part of any day.

"Darling," she says this evening, "I don't believe it, but I got it. I'm Bernadette."

"I knew they'd recognize your talent and dedication."

"Filming starts in three months."

"We'll be there long before that."

In December 1942 Bob and Bobby and Michael join Phyl in Hollywood and he quickly finds a job at MGM, the best studio, and will portray a tragic young soldier in *Bataan,* and on January second he tells Phyl, "The most important day of my life came five years ago when I met you. And today marks our fourth wedding anniversary. I pray we'll have fifty more years together."

"I hope so, too."

The new year starts slowly for Phyl, who is worried about having acted so little in recent years, and she tells Bob, "Sometimes I feel like I'm in a prison."

"We can change that," he says. "You're not Mr. Selznick's property. Let's go dancing. Let's eat in great restaurants. Let's take the kids to the beach and have some photos taken of our family."

"Mr. Selznick has forbidden that kind of publicity. He said people won't accept a virginal Bernadette who's married and has two children."

"Don't you think that's strange? All the other stars, and people like us trying to become stars, get as much publicity as the studios can generate."

"Really, Bob, we're both rather private people. Maybe Mr. Selznick is right."

"I need a little publicity to boost my career," he says.

"Not at the expense of my movie debut in this wonderful project."

After performing as Bernadette all day, Phyl studies her part every night at home.

"Guess what?" Bob says at dinner.

She doesn't respond.

"Can you hear me?"

"Yes," she says. "I wish you wouldn't disturb me."

"Thought you'd be interested. MGM's delighted how the audience responded to me in *Bataan*. They're giving me a new contract and the starring role in *See Here, Private Hargrove.*"

"Fine, Bob. Please help me practice this scene."

"Okay, and I'd sure like to see you do this on the set."

"I imagine you could get right in."

A couple of afternoons later he turns his motorcycle onto the lot of Twentieth Century-Fox. The guard at the gate asks, "Can I help you?"

"I'm Robert Walker, Jennifer Jones' husband. I've come to see her work in *The Song of Bernadette*."

"Wait here," says the man with a boxer's face. He walks into the guard hut, picks up the phone, says a few words and then listens before he returns to report, "That set is closed. No visitors or press."

"Please call the set. My wife will confirm everything."

"You're blocking traffic. You gotta leave."

Bob wants to argue but doesn't know what else to say. As he turns his motorcycle around, a chauffeured limousine passes by and he recognizes the rear passenger and waves and shouts, "Hello, Mr. Selznick. They won't let me in."

The great producer must not have seen or heard. He's already rolling through an open gate.

That night Bob tells Jennifer, "They wouldn't let me onto the lot today."

"Who wouldn't?"

"The guard. I told him who I was."

"Please, Bob, I'm tired and still have to practice my lines."

He's relieved when Phyl finishes playing Bernadette. She needs to relax. They take a short vacation and then sign to appear together in *Since You Went Away*. They'll be sweethearts. On Saturday night, two days before shooting begins, Phyl and Bob attend a Hollywood gala.

"It's so noisy and crowded," she says. "And people are staring at us."

"They can't help it. You look stunning."

"That's not what I mean."

"What's the matter?" he asks.

"Please take me home."

In their house Bob pays the babysitter who walks out the front door toward her home down the street. Phyl goes upstairs to check on the boys. He's standing by the fireplace when she returns and says, "Bob, please sit down."

He sits on the sofa and pats the place next to him. She instead sits in a chair, locks hands in her lap, and says, "I'm sure you're as unhappy as I am, Bob."

"I'm not unhappy at all, darling. You'll feel better now that you don't have to play a difficult character and carry an expensive movie in your debut."

"That's not it," she says.

"What else could it be? I know you were happy until *The Song of Bernadette.*"

"I'm not happy anymore."

Leaning forward, a forearm pressing each leg, he says, "You have a husband who loves you, two beautiful little boys, and the start of a great career in motion pictures."

"It's not the boys or my career, Bob."

"You're saying there's something wrong with me. Is that it?"

"You're nervous and unpleasant."

"Sometimes I'm a little tense, but I'm never unpleasant to you."

He feels his wife tighten before she says, "You certainly are."

"Just tell me what I'm doing that bothers you, and I promise I'll stop."

"I want you to move out, Bob."

Feeling like she punched him between the eyes, he says, "Phyl, you can't just throw me out. What about our family?"

"I've thought about this a long time and know it'll be better for both of us. The boys can visit you as much as they want."

"I insist you tell me what this is about."

"Please sleep on the sofa tonight. You can take whatever you need tomorrow."

Bob hugs the kids in the morning. They're too young to understand. He simply tells them, "Daddy's got to work far away some days."

Robert Walker is miserable in his little hotel room and needs a drink. Phyl only saw him drunk a few times, and the last time she said, "I'll leave if you ever do that again."

"I promise I won't," he said, and thereafter suppressed his periodic craving and wouldn't be opening a bottle of bourbon now if he weren't desperate. This Sunday night, his first alone, he takes a gulp from the bottle and then another and finds an old hotel glass and pours it full and drinks fast and feels a little relief and keeps drinking and as the room whirls he flops into bed and can't imagine why Phyl's stopped loving him and believes she may not have really stopped, she's just confused. The room spins faster and he's dreadfully nauseated and wakes up in the morning, bourbon caked to his face, wondering where the hell he is and then remembers and wishes he could forget.

Monday morning, he reports to the set of *Since You Went Away* and avoids people staring at his red eyes and pale and puffy face.

"Christ, Bob, what happened?" asks director Tay Garnett, placing a hand on his shoulder.

"Phyl threw me out," he says, covering his eyes with a hand.

"I'm sorry, Bob. Let me know if I can help."

"The only thing that can save me is getting Phyl back, and that's what I'm going to do."

There's a big party for cast and crew after the first day of shooting but Bob can't look into the camera or at Phyl standing at his side or David O. Selznick on the other side of Phyl or the other cast members. After the photo is taken, he looks up when Selznick says, "Hi, Bob, how're you doing?"

"Fine, sir."

He wants to speak privately and tell him about his sadness and ask to be replaced as Phyl's boyfriend but decides not to bother the busy producer.

Phyl and Bob don't have any scenes together during the first two weeks of shooting but most days he sees her walking on the lot, pretending not to notice him before she enters her large trailer for a star. He only has seventh billing and a small space but doesn't care about that. He wants to talk to his wife.

Tay Garnett sends a message to please visit him in his trailer right away. He's waiting at the door. "Hi, Bob, come on in and relax."

After they sit at opposite ends of a sofa, he says, "I'm damn sorry, Bob. The guy's a bastard but try to ignore studio gossip as much as you can."

"What gossip?"

"About Jennifer and Selznick."

"What about them?"

Tay looks uncomfortable. "I thought you'd have heard."

"What?"

"He's in love with her, and it looks like she's fallen for him."

Jolting to his feet, Bob says, "I can't fathom that. He's almost twenty years older and fat and gross."

"A lot of women in Hollywood overlook that stuff if guys have the power to make them stars."

"No," Bob shouts, and rushes out of the trailer and straight across the street to a bar and starts chugging shots that make his stomach and head hurt as much as his heart. On the way out, staggering, he sees a loser in a large ornate mirror and runs over and punches himself in the mouth and bloodies his hand and rips some tendons. The bartender calls the studio and someone drives Bob to the hospital and he can't work for more than a week.

When Bob returns, bearing a tender hand and severe hangover, Tay Garrett, without an appointment, appears at Selznick's office and tells the producer, "David, you've got to replace Bob. He's devastated."

"He's perfect for the part. More importantly, he makes Jennifer feel what her character needs to feel – a sense of loss."

"That's cruel."

"Get the hell out of my office."

In *Since You Went Away* the characters of Robert Walker and Jennifer Jones fall in love and Bob's real passion so upsets Jennifer that she sometimes cries and dashes off the set as cast and crew stare at the jilted husband who says, "Please tell me when Miss Jones is ready to resume," and sullenly walks out. Once, the actress refuses to open her trailer door, despite urgent requests from Tay Garnett and others in the production, and they summon David O. Selznick who, after minutes of effort, convinces the star to let him in.

"He keeps trying to win me back," she tells Selznick.

"You don't want him to, do you?"

"Of course not. I love you."

"You're on the verge of becoming the most popular actress in the world. Tap into Bob's passion."

Selznick stations himself behind the cameras for all scenes involving the estranged couple. Tay Garnett and others nearby sometimes hear the producer pant when Bob kisses Jennifer. The actor doesn't cry on set. He does that at home where he's often comforted by friend Jim Henaghan, a Hollywood journalist.

"I'd like to kill that guy," Bob says, finishing another drink. "He's spying on my wife and me. He can't stand that Phyl and I made love for years and are the parents of two children. I still think she loves me. Selznick's got her confused and overwrought."

"You're my buddy, and I'm going to be honest," Jim says. "My wife left me and so have a few girlfriends. I didn't get any of them back, whether I wanted to or not. There are lots of beautiful women in Hollywood who'd enjoy going out with a great guy who's also a damn fine actor. Get another woman. And stay off the booze."

"I'll quit drinking when Phyl comes home."

"Maybe you're better off without her."

"Go to hell," Bob says.

"I wasn't going to tell you, but I guess I've got to. Your wife is involved with a man who takes benzedrine and stays up all night gambling. He's lost more money than you or I'll ever make."

"I can't have my kids living with a guy like that."

"For the time being, he still lives with his wife Irene."

"What does the great Louis B. Mayer think about his son-in-law being unfaithful?" Bob asks.

"You think Mr. MGM's faithful? Guys like that don't give a damn."

Bob has rented an apartment in west Los Angeles and usually returns there right after shooting. He tries to relax by reading or listening to music, and sometimes he gets drunk and calls Phyl.

"It kills me you're sleeping with that guy," he tells her.

"Don't call me when you're drinking. In fact, don't call me at all unless it's about the boys."

"I'll call any damn time I want. Don't you have any pride, Phyl? He's got a button on his office desk that locks women in."

"That's a lie."

"He's unworthy of you."

Phyl hangs up. *Since You Went Away* ends with Bob's character going to war and dying. Phyl's character yearns for him but in life she usually arranges to be out when Bob comes by to pick up the boys. Several months later she's nominated for a best actress Oscar in *The Song of Bernadette*. Jim Henaghan calls Bob and says, "Hey, buddy, let's go to the Academy Awards ceremony next week."

"No thanks. That's Phyl's twenty-fifth birthday. I'll be staying home."

"You've got to start getting out, Bob."

"Not next week."

He sits in a reading chair, drinking and listening to the ceremony on radio, and when Phyl wins the Oscar he toasts her and says, "Congratulations, darling, I still love you," and throws his glass at an empty wall.

She earns another Oscar nomination for *Since You Went Away* and promptly files for a divorce that's granted in 1945. Robert Walker's movie success continues in a series of fine roles. Phyl is even more celebrated, earning an Oscar nomination in each of her first four years as a film actress.

"David O. Selznick," Bob shouts, startling the young woman he's dining with in a Hollywood restaurant. "How the hell could I compete with a giant like that? He was obsessed with my wife, so he stole her. I need another drink. How 'bout you?"

"No thanks," she says. "I work tomorrow and need to get to bed."

"Sure, at my place."

"No, take me home, please."

"Why on earth am I with a boring secretary when lots of exciting actresses want me?"

"Why am I having dinner with a drunken actor who only talks about his former wife?"

Bob slaps ten dollars on the table and says, "Take a cab."

The next night, he calls her and says, "I'm awfully sorry about my behavior. I'm really a nice fellow. I hope we can go out again sometime soon."

"Sorry, but I wouldn't feel comfortable with that."

Bob worries less about personal problems when he stars in *One Touch of Venus* in 1948. He's busy during the day, and after work costar Ava Gardner sometimes invites him to go out for a drink.

"She's the most gorgeous woman in Hollywood and a delight to work with," he tells Jim Henaghan.

"Be careful, Bob. She's already chewed up Mickey Rooney, and when Howard Hughes punched her in the jaw for screwing around, she flattened him with a poker to the head. There's a lot more I could tell you."

"I don't care. I fell in love with her the first night."

"You mean you've already… Take it easy, Bob, you're way too sensitive for her."

The following week, intent on a midday tryst, Bob is standing at her dressing room door, preparing to knock, when he hears Ava and a man talking and laughing. He then pounds the door and shouts, "Open up, goddamn it." The room grows quiet and the door stays closed. Bob steps down the hall and waits through lunch break and eventually sees stocky actor Howard Duff emerge from Ava's room and walk in the other direction. Bob stomps to her room and knocks and Ava says, "Back for more, Howard?" and unlocks the door he shoves open.

"Don't you have any morals?" Bob says.

"Sure I do. I'm in my dressing room and you aren't invited."

"When you made love to me, it meant something. I thought you felt the same way."

"We were just having fun, Bob."

"So you're as loose as people say."

"I don't care what people say."

"You're disgusting," he says and reaches for her but she backs away and he pursues.

"Get the hell out of my room," Ava orders, and he slaps her face, knocking her down.

"I'm so sorry," Bob says, and hurries out.

Late that afternoon Howard Duff searches the lot for Bob and when he finds him grabs his shirt with both hands and says, "I oughta belt you. Look at me. What the hell's the matter with you? You're falling apart."

Bob knows he's got to quit drinking before the weekend when Bobby and Michael will be staying with him. He's tense a few days but stays sober and is cleaned up and ready when they arrive on a Saturday morning. He takes them to the beach and then to eat hamburgers at a café near the water. Sunday evening he drives the boys back to their mother's home. She's lived in a mansion since her marriage to David O. Selznick, and Bob stares at the huge and elegant structure and thinks, "Somewhere in there my wife's screwing that guy..."

He drives home in a daze and calls Jim Henaghan and asks his friend to come over and when he arrives Bob tells him, "I'm sick of movies and the women who star in them."

"You ever consider going out with a lady who's just cute?" asks Jim. "Beautiful actresses are hard to deal with."

"You've known a few."

"Never lasts. Listen, John Ford's got a real nice daughter you should meet. I'm going to a party on his yacht next weekend. Join me."

Bob charms Barbara Ford and, after the director's yacht returns to the harbor, he takes her to his apartment and they're together every night. She meets and enjoys his children and introduces him to her father's buddies like John Wayne and they relax on yachts sailing to Catalina Island and a month after their first hello Bob says, "Let's get married."

"I've loved you since we met," she says, and kisses him hard on the mouth.

Barbara moves in, determined to transform Bob's place into a home. Their efforts are undermined when Phyl suddenly starts calling to insist he rush to stores and buy things for the children.

"Why don't you send some of Mr. Selznick's household staff," Bob finally says.

"They're all busy."

He silently nods when Barbara asks to go with him. Phyl's never home when Bob arrives with purchases received by servants. All this depresses him and he's silent on trips back to his house and once, eyes never leaving the road, he says, "Barbara, you're a pest."

"Please, let's talk when we get home."

Inside the front door she tries to embrace Bob but he pushes her to the tile floor and says, "Stay out of my bedroom."

He locks the door. Barbara knocks.

"Bob, I hope you aren't drinking again?"

He ignores her. She waits an hour before knocking again. There's still no response. Despite Bob's angry silence, Barbara every morning puts a tray of food on the floor by his bedroom door. Four days later he comes out.

"My parents are expecting us in Ogden," he says.

"That's wonderful, Bob. When do we leave?"

"You go. I couldn't stand it."

"I've done everything possible to please you," she says.

"Then shut up."

"You're the rudest man I've ever met."

Bob grabs each arm and shakes her and yells, "Shut up," jerking her side to side before throwing her down and yelling, "I mean it. Shut up."

He picks up a small old suitcase and leaves on a long drive to Ogden. Barbara runs to the phone and calls her father. He rushes over and picks her up and takes her to the family home. No one hears from Bob for two weeks. Barbara cries during dinner one night and John Ford says, "That bastard," and calls the wayward actor, who answers, "Yeah?"

"What the hell's wrong with you?"

"Nothing's wrong with me."

"You've got problems, Walker. I think Barbara's crazy, but she'll come back if you apologize and promise not to act like that again."

"She's never coming back. I want a divorce. Now."

Bob's excited to be out with another woman tonight, a lovely aspiring actress who doesn't complain that he's drinking fast even when the bartender says, "That's your last one, buddy. Go home and sleep it off."

They walk outside and she says, "Please give me your car keys, Bob."

"What for?"

"Because I can drive better."

"Fine, I need a chauffeur like you."

She may not be as drunk as Bob but speeds from the parking lot and is swerving when two officers in a patrol car pull them over.

"Step out of the car, please," an officer tells the actress.

"Leave her alone," Bob orders. "She's a nice lady driving me home."

"Pipe down," says the second officer, walking to the passenger door.

"Mind your manners or I'll kick both your asses," Bob says.

"Stay in the car," the first officer tells the actress and hustles to the passenger side and the two men yank Bob from the car.

"All right, wise guy, let's see you walk a straight line heel to toe," says the second officer.

Bob glances at each officer before running but in seconds he trips and falls and the officers arrest him and the actress.

"Don't waste our time," says the officer in charge of the booking desk. "Just admit you were drunk and disorderly."

Bob throws a weak punch that the officer blocks and several others converge and force him into a chair. He then notices a photographer and shouts, "Don't take my damn picture."

After spending several hours in a cell, Bob is released and calls a cab to take him where his car is parked. He slowly drives home, staggers inside, and drops into bed and stays there until evening when with difficulty he arises, walks to the front door, opens it and gingerly leans over to pick up the newspaper. The front page features a photo of angry and confused Robert Walker clenching his fist next to an untucked shirt.

He thinks MGM is going to fire him. They probably already have. He doesn't care. He'll leave this rotten town. But then he wouldn't get to see his boys. He couldn't endure that. In the morning he calls production chief Dore Schary, who says, "We need to have a talk."

Bob shaves and showers and drives to the MGM lot and a secretary ushers him into Schary's plush office. The newspaper photo and article lie on the executive's desk next to the actor's contract.

"Please sit down, Bob. We're all concerned about you. You're endangering yourself, and you're also damaging the studio."

"I promise this won't happen again."

"I don't think you can independently control that."

"I sure can. I'll quit drinking."

"Bob, we can tear up your contract," Schary says, placing his hand on it, "and you can quit acting and continue behavior that's certain to destroy you. Or you can enter the Menninger Clinic, the finest in the world, and undergo treatment until your problems are under control."

"How long would I be there?"

"As long as it takes. Doctors at Menninger tell me treatment can last a year or two."

"What about my boys?"

"They have a good home with their mother," says Schary.

"Yeah, and David O. Selznick."

"Think this over and let me know tomorrow."

Bob calls Dore Schary and says, "I'll go to Topeka and try the clinic but won't stay if I don't like it."

"That's entirely up to you. We'll pay for your treatment as long as you're there."

Robert Walker enters the Menninger Clinic on a cold Kansas day in December 1948 and immediately wants to escape a maze of locked doors and barred windows and the attendant who hands him a razor and watches him shave.

"When do I start treatment?" Bob asks the man.

"They usually just observe for a few weeks before starting therapy."

Each boring week seems longer than the last, and after a month Bob is desperate but performs the role of a relaxed man, telling his supervising doctor, "I simply need books, sir. I need them to read here at night, and I want to send some to my parents and my two boys. I know how to take care of myself. And I promise to return by late this afternoon. I've already checked the bus schedules."

"All right, Robert, take care, and call us if you need help."

In downtown Topeka, Bob doesn't feel like going to a bookstore. He'd just have to carry around a bunch of books all day. Better to find a warm bar and let bourbon relax him. He stops thinking about the clinic as he talks to a young man and his two younger female companions and they enjoy their drinks and want more and the other man says, "Let's go to the Central Hotel, best place in town."

"Okay," Bob says, smiling at the women.

On the way to the hotel, Bob's in the front seat and twisted around looking at his three new friends in back. They're loud in a crowded taxi, and the driver says, "Hold it down a little, will you?"

"No, we won't," says the man in back, sitting between the women.

"Either hold it down or get out and walk."

"We aren't getting out," Bob says.

The taxi driver, outnumbered four to one, quietly drives straight to the Central Hotel.

"That'll be seven bucks," he says.

"Like hell," says the man in back. "That was a five-minute ride."

"I'll give you two bucks," Bob says, handing him the money.

"Fine," the driver says, "but you still owe me five."

"You won't get any of that," says one of the women.

The taxi driver turns off the engine, takes his keys, and walks into the Central Hotel. He's already talking to a man behind the check-in desk when Bob's group enters and his buddy says, "This way to the bar."

A few minutes later, right after the drinks arrive, two police officers enter the bar. The taxi driver follows.

"Okay, let's hear your side of it," says one of the officers.

"We were being fleeced," says Bob's buddy.

The officer nods toward the driver. "He told us you were all drunk and unruly and refused to get out of his taxi like he told you."

Bob stands and says, "Move on or I'll kick your butts."

The police grab and handcuff Bob and arrest all four revelers. At the station they silently sit, waiting to be booked, until Bob shoots from his chair and runs across the room to a glass-covered bulletin board and punches it with each fist, shattering glass and tearing flesh from his hands and wrists. The nearest officer grabs Bob but the actor pushes him to the floor and thrashes another glass-covered bulletin board and three officers tackle and hold him down while one yells, "Get an ambulance."

Another officer asks Bob, "What're you doing in Topeka?"

"I'm, I'm visiting friends, family and friends."

The officer studies Bob for several seconds. "Are you staying at the Menninger Clinic, sir?"

"Yeah, but just for observation. I don't have any serious problems."

"Have Menninger send a doctor over," the officer tells his colleagues.

A staff psychiatrist arrives and takes Bob to the hospital to get sewn up with a hundred stitches. Then they return to the clinic. In the morning a doctor asks Bob, "Do you remember what happened downtown yesterday?"

"No," he says, staring at bandaged hands and arms.

The doctor gives Bob the details, reveals that charges have been dropped, and arranges a phone conversation with Dore Schary.

"I'm not crazy, Mr. Schary. But this place is causing me problems. I've got to get out of here."

"Bob, you can force your way out, legally, but I urge you to stay. Be honest with yourself. You need help. And the doctors think you're ready to start therapy. Give it a try."

Robert Walker decides to stay and talk about his feelings every day.

"My mother was like ice," he says. "Even now she won't admit I'm a success in films. My father won't tell me, either, but I think he'd like to… They thought I was a disturbed kid and threw me out when I was thirteen and made me go to military school far from home… After that I was accepted by the American Academy of Dramatic Arts in New York. That's where I met the most incredible woman, Phyllis Isley. She's my wife. She was. A powerful producer became obsessed and lured her away… Sure, I've gone out with other women since then, but no one matches Phyl… I can't imagine she's with an old man like Selznick… I married another woman but she was inferior to Phyl, so I threw her out. That divorce was final last week. I'd like to get married again. I think I can have another good marriage if I find the right woman and quit drinking… I need to relax sometimes, but alcohol hurts more than helps…"

Dore Schary calls Bob once or twice a week and, without telling the actor, also regularly talks to relevant doctors.

"Bob is making remarkable progress, Mr. Schary," says Bob's primary psychiatrist. "I wasn't optimistic at first, but now, following six months of therapy, he understands many of his problems. Although Bob may someday need a little more treatment, we believe he has recovered and is ready to be released and return to work."

"That's wonderful," says Schary. He immediately calls Bob and tells him, "Congratulations, your colleagues and I are anxious to see you. And don't worry, we'll start you with one or two roles that aren't emotionally demanding."

"Oh, that's not necessary, Mr Schary. I'm ready for any part."

"See you soon, Bob."

Late on a Friday afternoon in May 1949, Bob drives and parks in front of the Selznick mansion in Beverly Hills and hops out and opens his arms as Bobby and Michael dash to embrace him. They would've forgotten their suitcases if the maid hadn't hustled out with one in each hand.

"Wait till you see the place I got us in Pacific Palisades," he says.

"Does it have a pool?" Bobby asks.

"You bet it does."

"Are we close to the beach?" asks Michael.

"About a five-minute drive."

The boys shout, "Let's go," and their father leads them into summer adventures of hiking and fishing and swimming. Bob also stars in two light comedies and proves, to studio executives and himself, that his acting skills haven't eroded.

When the soothing summer ends, Bobby and Michael return to live with their mother, and Bob starts accepting overtures from several women he casually dates but there's no spark and he sometimes drinks and says things he regrets. He still yearns for Phyl, and when the phone rings and he hears her say, "Hello, Bob," he thinks she may be tired of David O. Selznick.

"Hiya, Phyl. How've you been?"

"I prefer to be called Jennifer."

"Of course, that's the special name bestowed by your Svengali."

"I didn't call to argue, simply to tell you that I'm taking the boys to Europe soon."

"That'll be a great vacation."

"This would be a semi-permanent move, Bob. I intend to enroll them in a private Swiss school. David and I must live in Europe since most of his business is there now."

"I hope he has better luck there than in the United States. I keep reading he's selling off his movie equipment."

Phyl hangs up, and Bob dreads living thousands of miles from his sons. Before long Phyl learns she won't be leaving for a while. She must take a role she doesn't want to help her husband, who keeps selecting lackluster film projects and popping benzedrine while he gambles all night.

Bob would like to have primary custody of the boys but knows he can't always handle the stress. Right now, overwhelmed by something he doesn't understand, he phones Dore Schary who arranges a call from MGM chief Louis B. Mayer.

"I'm doing very well, Mr. Mayer," says Bob. "It's great to be back at work. But I feel I need another month or so of therapy at the Menninger Clinic."

"You don't need to go to Kansas for therapy," says Mayer, a fatherly figure when it suits him. "Beverly Hills has more psychiatrists than any place in the world. And they're damn good."

"Which one do you recommend?"

"Lots of people in our business go to Dr. Frederick Hacker. Give him a call."

"Thanks, I will," says Bob, who promptly dials the distinguished doctor and tells his secretary, "Good morning, this is Robert Walker. I've got to see Dr. Hacker right away, but I'm too tense to drive."

"I'll check with the doctor and call you back."

"Please hurry. My phone number's…"

She tells the doctor, "Robert Walker needs help. It sounds like an emergency."

"The actor?" he asks.

"It sounds like him."

He immediately calls Bob and asks, "Where are you? Fine, just stay at home. I can be there in about two hours. Is that soon enough?"

"Yeah, my address is…"

Before leaving his office, the doctor phones Dore Schary and discusses Bob's personal history and treatment.

"Thank you for coming, Dr. Hacker," says Emily, Bob's housekeeper. "Mr. Walker's in a lot of pain. He often gets so wound up. I hope your psychoanalysis can help him. He's in the bedroom."

Stretched stiff on his back in bed, Bob tries to get up but is unable to.

"Hi, Bob, I'm Dr. Hacker. Can you tell me when this disturbance began?"

"About ten years ago, maybe all my life."

"I mean your current level of discomfort."

"A few hours ago. I've gotta have something now."

"I understand, Bob. May I use your phone to call Dr. Sidney Silver? He's an expert in sedation."

"Sure, tell him to hurry."

In less than an hour Dr. Silver is standing in Bob's living room with Dr. Hacker, and Emily's listening from the kitchen.

"He's already had months of therapy, Sidney."

Dr. Silver nods. "I've heard that."

From his bed Bob shouts, "Are you guys going to talk all afternoon or help me?"

"We'll be right there, Bob," says Dr. Hacker.

"I think we better intervene medically," Dr. Silver says.

"I agree. What medication do you recommend?"

"Sodium amytal," says Dr. Silver.

They enter the bedroom and Dr. Hacker says, "We're going to make you feel better, Bob."

"I doubt that's possible."

Dr. Silver finishes loading his syringe and says, "I promise this will help, Bob," and finds a large vein in the crook of the arm and pushes a long smooth dose into the aggrieved actor.

In minutes Bob looks at the doctors and almost smiles. "This stuff's pretty good."

"No need to suffer," says Dr. Hacker. "We can help you whenever you need it."

Bob soon meets a kind young woman, actress Kay Scott, who adores him and he feels the same about her. He sees Bobby and Michael often, and is convinced his next role, as wicked Lee Strobie in *Vengeance Valley*, will be his most challenging. Production starts in July 1950 in Colorado.

He calls Phyl and says, "We'll only be on location about a month, Phyl. Please let me take the boys. They'd love hiking and fishing in the mountains."

"The boys adore you, Bob, and I know you love them," she says. "But I'm concerned about your condition."

"Don't worry. I've got great doctors and a wonderful new medication."

"The doctors aren't going with you to Colorado, are they?"

"No, but they've given me some oral medications in case I need a little help. I'll hire a babysitter to keep an eye on Bobby and Michael when I'm working."

"All right, Bob. Please be careful."

"I will, I promise."

Off camera in Colorado, when Bob and his sons aren't exploring the Rocky Mountains, he enjoys talking to dashing Burt Lancaster who stars as Owen, his foster brother. No longer is Bob playing a polite and likable guy people want as a friend. His character is a lifelong louse who loafs on his wealthy father's cattle ranch and borrows money he doesn't repay and cheats on his wife and impregnates another woman and schemes to steal his father's cattle and leave the region after he leads Owen into an ambush. Bob enjoys using new dramatic skills and is soon gratified by his strong reviews and *Vengeance Valley*'s popularity at the box office.

Kay Scott hopes Bob's professional success will help keep him stable, and they continue to blend friendship and romance. But one evening at her house he refuses to talk, and she asks, "What's wrong?"

"I don't know. It's that thing. Maybe I better go home and call my doctors."

"Would they come on a Saturday night?"

"Sure, for what I pay them."

Kay presses her cheek to Bob's and embraces him on the sofa and says, "Call and tell them to come here tonight."

"Thanks," he says. "And don't worry, I never need this more than once a month."

The following week, in his MGM office, Dore Schary receives a call from Alfred Hitchcock.

"I suppose you've heard, Dore, that I shall soon make a picture from the most intriguing property I've ever had – *Strangers on a Train.*"

"Everyone's talking about it, Hitch. You and Warner Brothers are lucky."

"I'll be fortunate only if I obtain the services of the singular actor qualified to play diabolical Bruno Antony."

"Half the actors in town would love the role," Schary says.

"Their aspirations are irrelevant. Only Robert Walker is suitable for the part, and Warners will compensate you handsomely for his services."

"I'm sure we can make a deal."

Hitchcock smiles into the receiver. "I admire his portrayal of evil in *Vengeance Valley* and know he'll be even more demonic as Bruno Antony. I've been reading about Robert, and talking to some who know him, and am convinced his personal life will enhance this role.

I'll send him a copy of Patricia Highsmith's book."

Bob is stunned but delighted by the esteemed director's offer and eagerly reads what he realizes is the best dramatic role of his career. When the screenplay arrives, he studies his part and everyone else's and refines his expressions and gestures.

Hitchcock takes Bob and costar Farley Granger to shoot some scenes near New York City in October 1950, and the following month, prior to interior filming in Burbank, the director invites the two actors to his house for dinner. At a long dining table, Hitchcock says, "Gentlemen, let's discuss your parts."

"You aren't like Bruno Antony in real life, are you, Bob?" Granger asks.

Bob laughs, putting a hand on his stomach and leaning forward, and Hitchcock says, "Perhaps we should cast you in a comedy."

"This role is more stimulating."

"Your enthusiasm is essential, for this story must be driven by villainous Robert Walker, whom onscreen we shall call Bruno Antony. I hope this emphasis doesn't bother you, Farley."

"Not at all. I'm motivated that my character starts as a relaxed fellow and changes into a frightened and desperate man."

Hitchcock clears his throat. "I have every shot intricately mapped out and am certain you gentlemen are ready for sublime performances."

When the cameras roll, Alfred Hitchcock sees Robert Walker magically portray wealthy and weird Bruno Antony on a train where he recognizes star amateur tennis player Guy Haines, played by Granger, and starts a pleasant conversation, asking genial questions, and then makes too many personal comments including that he's read Guy wants a divorce so he can marry his girlfriend, the daughter of a senator. Bruno reveals he sometimes wants to kill the rich father who hates him and asks Guy if he wants to hear about a perfect crime. They could simply "swap murders," implying Bruno would murder Guy's wife and Guy, in return, would kill Bruno's father. There's nothing to worry about, Bruno explains. They couldn't be implicated since neither has a motive.

Appalled, Guy hurries to exit the train.

Bruno, gripped by mental illness, doesn't understand he has no deal and strangles Guy's unfaithful wife and then shocks him with news of the deed as well as the demand that Guy fulfill his obligation. Guy refuses, but Bruno Antony isn't finished. He's lurching toward more violence, and Robert Walker's performance rivets cast and crew. Upon the film's release, numerous audiences and critics declare the work "brilliant... disturbing... chilling..." and many in Hollywood believe Bob will receive an Oscar nomination.

Dore Schary receives the results and calls Bob to say, "It doesn't matter you weren't selected, Bob. Your portrayal of Bruno has already earned a prominent place in film history."

"I know Humphrey Bogart deserved to win because of his work in *The African Queen,* but I'm let down because I'll never find another character as fascinating as Bruno Antony."

"On the contrary, Bob. You're poised for an exceptional career."

Bob knows he should be happy about his acting and great kids and his courtship of sweet Kay Scott, but he's consumed by something excruciating and starts calling Dr. Hacker more often.

"My head's hurting again, Doc. Please come and fix it."

"Keep in mind, Bob, that we must be careful when administering sodium amytal. It can be dangerous."

"How much are you giving me?"

"Dr. Silver started you at two and a half grains. Later, when you've been particularly agitated, he's given you up to seven and a half grains. That's the limit."

"I promise I won't ask for more."

"You haven't been drinking, have you, Bob?"

"Not tonight."

"Don't ever drink before taking this medication. Dr. Silver and I will be over within the hour."

In the spring of 1951, Bob starts filming *My Son John* and shortly tells Kay Scott, "Honey, I hate making this pseudo-patriotic nonsense.

Imagine, my character is condemned by his mother because he falls in love with a communist. Naturally, she's a spy. Spies are everywhere, and they all hate God. The damn director sermonizes all the time when he should be refining the script. I pray Hitchcock wants me for another movie soon."

"He will, sweetheart," she says.

During their summer vacation, Bobby and Michael are invited by a friend and his parents to visit and camp for two weeks. They leave in mid-August when Bob has finished most of his scenes and won't be needed for a month. He misses the boys right away. They're his beach buddies. And what's he supposed to do when Kay's working? He needs another film fast but will have to wait. Time's passing slowly and he wishes he weren't so damn sad.

It's a distressingly gray and rainy late afternoon on August twenty-eighth in west Los Angeles, and Emily hears Bob say, "Get out of my head, for god's sake," and she rushes into his bedroom. "Are you all right, Mr. Walker?"

Lying on his back in bed, he says, "Get me a drink."

"You know you're not supposed to."

"I've got to have something."

"What's the matter?"

"Same as always. Now get me a drink."

"I will not, Mr. Walker."

He climbs out of bed and lunges toward the door. She tries to block him, but he pushes her aside and staggers into the kitchen and shouts, "Where'd you hide the liquor, Emily?"

"You and Jim Henaghan drank it all last night."

"Go get some more."

"No," she says.

"Where are my car keys?"

"I don't know, Mr. Walker."

"Did you hide those, too?"

"Maybe Jim took them. I hope so."

Bob flings himself on the bed and plunges his face in a pillow before he twists onto his side in fetal position and says, "Don't you understand? Call me a cab."

"No sir."

"I'll call my own."

"Stay in bed, Mr. Walker," Emily says, rushing toward the living room phone. "I'm calling Dr. Hacker."

The psychoanalyst for the stars arrives in forty-five minutes and his associate, Dr. Silver, rushes in shortly thereafter. He proceeds to Bob's bedroom where Dr. Hacker is trying to hold his patient's shoulders to stop him from jerking around or getting up.

"Please settle down so we can help you, Bob," says Dr. Hacker.

"I don't want any more needles. I need a drink."

"You can't drink and take this medication," Dr. Hacker says.

Bob pushes Hacker away and sits up in bed and says, "I'm gonna get the hell out and have some fun."

"You're not going anywhere, Bob," says Dr. Silver.

"Get out of my way."

Dr. Hacker tells his colleague, "We better have him hospitalized."

"He'll be all right, if we can get him to take his medicine."

"I told you, no more of that," Bob says, and grabs one of Hacker's hands with both of his while Silver steps to the opposite side and pushes Bob's shoulders to the mattress but can't keep them there.

"What the hell's going on?" shouts Jim Henaghan, entering the bedroom.

"Identify yourself, sir" says Dr. Hacker.

"I'm Bob Walker's best friend."

"He and Bob have been close for years," Emily confirms, standing near the door and looking almost as frightened as Bob.

"Your friend needs a shot to calm him down," says Dr. Hacker.

"Bob, do you want the shot?" asks Henaghan.

"Hell no. I'm leaving."

"How're going to do that?" Henaghan asks.

"I'm driving. Give me my car keys."

"I don't have them."

"Fine, give me yours."

"You aren't driving, Bob," Henaghan says, and looks steadily at Dr. Hacker and then at Dr. Silver. "Gentleman, does my buddy really need this shot?"

"He certainly does," says Dr. Hacker. "Otherwise, we'll have to hospitalize him, and that may require a straitjacket."

"What do you want me to do?"

"Hold him down so I can administer the shot."

Henaghan says, "All right, buddy, just relax" and presses his two hundred pounds on the actor. "Don't worry. This won't hurt."

"Let me up, you bastard."

Dr. Silver loads his syringe, steps in, and after two unsuccessful jabs finds a vein and pushes in sodium amytal. He steps back and watches with the two other men and Emily as Bob closes his eyes. Five seconds, ten, fifteen, twenty…

"Hey, he's not breathing," says Henaghan.

Dr. Silver leans over the bed and places his ear to Bob's mouth.

"Sidney, is he breathing?" asks Dr. Hacker, hovering over the foot of the bed.

"I don't think so."

Dr. Silver forces Bob's mouth open and begins mouth-to-mouth resuscitation while Dr. Hacker rushes into the living room and calls the fire department emergency squad. Jim Henaghan takes one of Bob's hands and squeezes and says, "Come on, buddy. Don't give up." By the time the rescue squad and police arrive, Henaghan and Emily are seated in the bedroom, crying, and the doctors are pacing the living room.

"I better call the coroner," says Dr. Hacker.

The police have dismissed the emergency workers and are talking to the doctors when the coroner arrives and takes over and asks, "What did you give him?"

"Sodium amytal," says Dr. Silver.

"How much?"

"Seven and a half grains," Dr. Silver says.

"That's quite a bit," says the coroner.

"We've given him sodium amytal at least thirty times during the last year, and he's always responded very well," says Dr. Hacker. "This dosage is indicated when a patient is violent and out of control."

"Had he been drinking?" the coroner asks.

"We saw no signs of drinking," says Hacker.

"Did you see him drink, ma'am?" the coroner asks.

"Nothing since late last night," says Emily.

The coroner turns to the doctors and says, "I presume you know that late-night drinking often leaves one intoxicated until the following afternoon or evening."

"This was an emergency," says Dr. Hacker. "We had no time to inquire about his activities the previous night."

"I may order an autopsy," says the coroner.

"There's no need for that," Dr. Hacker says.

"None whatsoever," says Dr. Silver.

"All right," says the coroner, "no autopsy unless the family demands it."

Power Couple

Walter Wanger reads fine books and often gives copies to friends who appreciate his literary insights. Movie moguls also respect his judgment and hire him to produce films of distinction. He earns much money and, as a handsome and distinguished man, romances actresses and other ladies and sometimes reminds his wife she agreed to an open arrangement.

He's always on the lookout for talented actors he thinks he can turn into stars and is now delighted to shape the career of Joan Bennett who's stunning even by Hollywood standards. She's also a competent actress whose father Richard was, until weakened by drink, one of the most celebrated stage actors and whose sister Constance was, for a short time, the highest paid performer in movies.

Joan's progress is commendable, but Walter knows she can do more. Late this evening in her new Holmby Hills mansion, he kisses her cheek and neck and says, "Darling, I want you to trust me."

"I will when your divorce is final and you marry me."

"Perhaps someday, but I wouldn't change my habits."

Joan pushes his hands away and says, "It's quite late."

"We have something important to discuss."

"Not marriage, evidently."

"Something even more exciting."

Suspicious eyes examine Walter before she says, "What?"

"I want you to become a brunette. It will transform your career."

"That's absurd, Walter. Women yearn to be blondes."

"We start filming *Trade Winds* in two weeks. After your blond character shoots a man and dyes her hair to escape, we'll compare the two Joans and see who audiences prefer."

Brunette Joan Bennett smolders on screen and her confidence soars. Soon, after a 1938 celebration in her home, she embraces Walter and says, "I hope you've already found something else right for me."

"Haven't had a chance. John Ford won't leave me alone. He wants me to produce *Stagecoach* starring John Wayne."

"John Wayne can't act," scoffs Joan.

"He certainly can."

Director Ford agrees with Wanger, declaring that John Wayne's going to be the biggest star in movie history, and many others praise a film that earns seven Oscar nominations and wins two.

Joan's appearing in less prestigious films but is in demand and can afford private schools for two daughters from previous marriages and pay the mortgage and several servants to maintain her home and take care of the children.

"I have so much, Walter, but I don't have a husband," she says.

"I love you but don't think we need bourgeois formalities. Guess who called me today?"

"Who?"

"Alfred Hitchcock. He wants to direct *Foreign Correspondent.*"

"I'm available for the female lead, Walter. I admire his work."

"I know, and you'd be wonderful, but Hitch prefers Joan Fontaine. I doubt her studio will loan her to us, so I've got to find someone soon. I'm afraid I'll be looking every night this week."

Joan simmers several seconds before saying, "You seem to have more late meetings than anyone in town. I hope you're busy Saturday night because Errol Flynn wants to take me dancing."

"What did you tell the great ladies' man?"

"I said I'd see. And now that I have, I'll tell him to pick me up at six."

"Trying to make me jealous, Joan?"

"I'd like to ask you a question, Walter. What are you doing to me?"

Joan and Errol Flynn don't last long but she's often asked out and dates several men. Nevertheless, she soon tells Walter, "I need to see you more often."

"I'm shocked you'd have time, given your hectic schedule."

Several nights later in Joan's home, after the children are in bed, Walter tells her, "I have something to tell you."

Joan takes one of his hands in both hers. "What is it?"

"John Ford's been calling again."

"About what?"

"He wants me to produce *The Long Voyage Home*. John Wayne's also interested."

"Oh, the big star John Wayne?"

"He dominates every room he enters, Joan."

"A pity he isn't more talented."

"After *The Long Voyage Home*, I think you'll appreciate his appeal."

The movie garners six Oscar nominations and numerous good reviews but loses money.

"Great news, Joan," says Walter. "You can star in my next picture – *The House Across the Bay*. You'd enjoy working with George Raft and Walter Pidgeon. Both are doing quite well now."

"I'll take the role, Walter, just for you."

This clumsy melodrama about lust, racketeering, escape from Alcatraz, and murder bores viewers and costs more than it nets.

"Don't worry," Joan tells Walter. "Your next pictures will do better."

"At the moment, I'm not thinking about business."

"What's on your mind?"

"That we're forever."

"Just the two of us?"

"I'll try," he says.

In early 1940 at age twenty-nine Joan Bennett marries for the third time. Her new husband is still attractive at forty-five and delighted to move into Joan's mansion and live with her daughters, whom he treats with respect and affection. The couple keep making movies and serve on a committee urging President Franklin Roosevelt to help Jews being persecuted in Europe.

At least once a day Joan's chauffeur drives to her movie studio or location and delivers the cook's shopping list which she studies before adding or deleting items and writing instructions about how everything must be prepared. She also reads messages phoned by her secretary, who Joan promptly calls. Everything must be perfect for their elegant dinner parties.

At work Joan strives to improve her craft under the direction of talented but tyrannical German refugee Fritz Lang. Their first film, *Man Hunt*, emerges as a slow and unpersuasive story about a man who tries to kill Hitler.

She makes other films that leave her unfulfilled but is delighted to bear her third daughter and first child with Walter in 1944. They hire another nanny so Joan can report to the set of *The Woman in the Window*, which Fritz Lang directs like a feudal lord.

"No, no, Joan," he says in heavy Teutonic accent. "You must show exactly the emotions I tell you, and you must move the way I tell you, and you must not do anything unless I tell you why you must do it."

"I'll do just as you say, Fritzie, because I know I'm improving."

Charismatic Edward G. Robinson plays a professor who takes a late-night stroll and encounters a beautiful portrait in a gallery window and, as he gazes, the divine subject, Joan's character Alice, eases close to him, enchanting the professor, and they depart for drinks and then to her luxurious apartment where the man paying for the place arrives unexpectedly and presumes the visitor, despite being short and pudgy, is seducing his mistress, and the big boyfriend attacks and pounds the intruder who survives when Joan hands him scissors he plunges into the boyfriend's back. Logical people would call the police, explain what happened, and prove self-defense. But that would preclude dramatic possibilities, since the professor is married and would be wrecked by scandal, so they scramble to hide the facts and become targets of an extortionist, smoothly portrayed by Dan Duryea, and a vigorous police investigation. The professor decides he has no escape except suicide. Rather than disappoint moviegoers who sympathize with the avuncular star, there's a surprise resolution.

"You could've been better, Joan" says Walter.

"I think I performed rather well."

"Robinson was great."

"Certainly," she says. "It was his movie."

"Next time you work with Lang, I'll produce the picture and protect your dramatic interests."

"You hate creative arguments, Walter. Focus on the business end."

Fritz Lang marches onto the 1945 set of *Scarlet Street* as if he were a conquering general. Joan is receptive to his endless critiques, but Walter, who often visits the set, approaches the director one evening after work.

"Fritz, this is a great opportunity to stretch Joan's dramatic abilities as a treacherous woman," he says.

"That I am doing," says Lang.

"I want Joan to have more dialogue and close-ups."

"I'm the director."

"And, like you, Joan and I each own one-third of this enterprise."

"Go back to your office," says Lang.

"Fine, but we'll be talking soon if you misuse my wife."

That evening Joan tells Walter, "I want you two to get along so you don't ruin the best role I've ever had."

At work the next morning Lang asks Joan, "Does your husband believe I listen to anything he says?"

"He admires you so much, Fritzie."

"He certainly should."

Joan again teams with Edward G. Robinson and Dan Duryea, and her character, Kitty, pretends to love Chris, a married painter portrayed by Robinson. He's smitten and allows her to take credit for his work. A major art critic deems "her" paintings wonderful, generating many high-priced sales, and Kitty secretly keeps the money. Chris walks in as she's embracing her clever but dastardly sidekick Johnny, played by Duryea, and Kitty later mocks him as a dreary old man she could never love. This plunges Chris into knife-wielding rage. Surprisingly, in an era of tight moralistic censorship, Johnny is wrongly electrocuted, but arbiters of the Production Code decide Chris will suffer enough as a homeless man watching his paintings sell for thousands.

A few years after World War II, television weakens the box office and actors' salaries often decline, but Walter and Joan still manage to live at her beautiful Holmby Hills estate and welcome their second daughter and Joan's fourth.

"Time for another big picture with Fritz Lang," Walter says.

"What is it?"

"*Secret Beyond the Door.* Here it is," he says, handing her the script. "A man may be planning to murder his wife."

On the set Fritz Lang orders most people around as if he were a monarch. Joan nevertheless feels she has the status to privately tell him, "I think some of my lines need reworking."

"You know Silvia Richards is a brilliant screenwriter," Lang says. "We discuss the script every night and every morning."

"I wonder if that's the best arrangement, professionally speaking."

"When she writes, she speaks for me."

"Fritzie, Walter's on my side. This story doesn't move fast enough."

"You'll follow my instructions, and so will your husband."

Creative tension fails to enliven a script mired in quicksand, and Walter again produces an unprofitable film. Several weeks later, examining recent financial statements, Joan says, "Pease be careful, Walter. I could lose the house."

"That won't happen. I'm going to make a film classic – *Joan of Arc.*"

For two years he labors to assemble cast and crew and hires Victor Fleming, who had directed *Gone with the Wind.*

A week before filming starts, Joan tells her husband, "I'm a fool taking a half million out of my home to finance your strange picture."

"I've got money in this house, too."

"Not like I do."

"I've got the most compelling actress in the world today."

"Yes," says Joan, "Ingrid Bergman's undoubtedly the finest 'kitchen maid' in the business."

"She's beautiful and wholesome. People love her."

Production is slow, expensive, and unpromising, and moviegoers don't like the turgid spectacle, and the Wangers get trounced.

"Just relax, Joan," says Walter, "nobody's going to repossess our home."

"How could you spend the most ever on a film without any stars except Bergman?" she asks.

Ingrid Bergman also alienates many bluenose moviegoers in the United States when she deserts her husband and moves to Italy with Roberto Rossellini and bears his child. Walter Wanger, the playboy producer, telegrams Bergman that she's to blame for box office woes, and he demands she proclaim herself a moral woman if indeed she is one.

Bergman ignores him.

Chronically tired and nervous, Walter calls directors but they don't respond. At Hollywood events he looks hopefully at producers who avert their eyes. Actors and actresses stop approaching. Depressed and financially dependent on his wife's labor, Walter despairs when his friend and frequent dinner guest, and president of the bank holding Joan's loan, forecloses on the home.

"Do you always have to be so glum, Walter?" Joan says.

"You'd feel the same."

"I'm losing a lot."

"But you've still got your name and a place in the industry. I can't even get a job."

Joan's dynamic agent, Jennings Lang, calls and asks to discuss her career over lunch. They meet in a small restaurant off Sunset Boulevard.

"You're lovely, Joan, but in your early forties. We have to consider other options. I think television would be ideal. It's a new world."

"I want to be on the big screen."

"That's fine, but please remember millions are watching that small screen."

"All right," she says. "Is there somewhere we can discuss this privately?"

"Yes, a friend at work left me the key to a vacant apartment. It's a nice place."

"Have you been there?" she asks.

"Oh, no. Based on what he said."

Joan and Jennings drive separately to the apartment and enter together. Three hours later she tells him, "I never feel like this at home."

They meet once or twice a week during 1951 in Los Angeles and sometimes rendezvous in faraway locales. Upon returning from her latest vacation, Joan faces an irritable Walter who demands, "Where have you been?"

"I told you, visiting friends in New York."

"I hear you were in the Caribbean and not alone."

"That's ridiculous."

"What's going on between you and Jennings?"

"Same thing you've been doing all your life," she says, spinning to leave the room and over her shoulder snapping, "I'm going out."

Walter wonders where she's going. She doesn't have work this afternoon. He thinks it's unreasonable she expects him to stay home and care for their daughters. He needs to get out and make deals, but Hollywood only likes guys on top. Joan doesn't say it. She doesn't have to. She considers Jennings Lang way ahead of Walter. For the moment, he is, but Walter plans to recover and make great movies.

In a little while he leaves home, driving fast, and in minutes is jarred seeing his wife's car in the agency's parking lot. He drives around an hour and her car's still there and his stomach hurts after another long drive nowhere reveals the car unmoved and Walter loses his last thread of hope and admits Joan is somewhere private with Jennings Lang.

Pulling into the lot, the producer parks and waits.

In a half hour the agent drives in and parks before he exits and escorts Joan to her car where they embrace and kiss and talk before Joan gets in and he leans in her window and they're nuzzling when Walter charges from his car. He doesn't see Joan's expression. He's locked onto Jennings Lang who turns and extends both palms, urging, "Walter, Walter, for god's sake settle down."

Joan shouts, "Walter," the same moment he fires a shot and then

another, and then she shouts, "Get out of here," and rushes out of her
car to help the fallen Lang, who an ambulance soon rushes to a hospital.

Walter walks to his car and waits for the police and at the station
explains he was protecting his family. Elsewhere in the building, a
detective asks, "What were you doing, Mrs. Wanger?"

"It's Miss Bennett."

"What were you doing in that parking lot?"

"I was sitting in my car."

"And what else?"

"Talking to my agent."

"And what were you talking about."

"Movies."

"Where were you before you and your agent returned to the
parking lot."

"We had lunch."

"Your husband said your car was parked in the agent's lot for a few
hours. What were you two doing besides lunch?"

"We only had lunch and discussed business."

"That's doubtful," says the detective.

"I beg your pardon," she counters.

Fortunately for Jennings Lang as well as Walter, one of the bullets
missed and the other hit pavement before ricocheting into Lang's groin
but missing vital organs, and he recovers after surgery.

Walter hires Jerry Giesler, a renowned Hollywood troubleshooter, to
defend him. After examining evidence and negotiating with the district
attorney, Giesler tells Walter to plead guilty and serve a few months in
minimum security north of town and he does so in obscurity.

"I'm thankful to be back home, Joan."

"It's over," she says.

"I still love you."

"I don't think you ever did."

"Are you throwing me out?"

"Not out of the house. Only my bedroom. From now on, we're

roommates caring for our children."

Joan has a movie out now, *Father of the Bride,* and soon its sequel, each with Spencer Tracy. Both receive good reviews and audience responses, but producers banish her because of "immoral behavior" and the press and public also express indignation. By contrast, Walter is embraced by Hollywood powerbrokers as well as the press and public, and they help him recover and in two years he makes a gritty and popular film, *Riot in Call Block 11,* and soon follows with *Invasion of the Body Snatchers,* which becomes a cult classic.

Joan isn't offered anything for three years until *Highway Dragnet,* a B-minus movie in which she portrays a strap murderess who specializes in strangulation. She realizes films will no longer support her and, often leaving one or both her youngest daughters with Walter and nannies, moves to New York to accept roles in major plays touring the nation. She falls for an actor and wants to marry him but he has a heart attack. Next, she's in love with an actor who looks so much like John Barrymore he's rumored to be the Great Profile's illegitimate son. Before long she cares for him as he's devoured by cancer.

Back in Los Angeles, the debt-ridden actress sells her huge home and buys a stylish but smaller place that forces her closer to frowning Walter.

"I want a divorce," she tells him.

"I won't give it to you," he says.

"Why not?"

"I need to be part of a family," he says.

"You're a marvelous housewife," Joan says, and walks out.

She makes countless phone calls, tapping a sea of contacts, and takes as many parts as possible. And from a series of New York apartments, she calls Walter to issue the recurrent demand.

"If you try to divorce me, Joan, I'll make sure your name stays in the scandal sheets."

"You're a pitiful man who, incidentally, is aging rather rapidly," she says.

During theater breaks Joan sometimes returns to their unhappy home in California.

"Let's quit living a lie," she urges Walter.

"I prefer this arrangement to the alternative."

Then, when it looks like they'll hurt each other forever, Walter swoons for a young woman and tells Joan, "I've contacted my attorney, and we can end this marriage."

"At last."

MASS MURDER

The Educator

Vincent Brothers grew up in the Long Island home of his mother who worked hard but also needed welfare to support ten children. The father was often absent and never much help except, perhaps, when he told young Vincent, "Learn to make money or you'll end up on the streets or worse."

"I promise I'm gonna be rich, Daddy."

Vincent dutifully attended all his classes and, after wrestling practice, hurried home to study and always earned good grades. The family delighted that he was the first to go to college. At Norfolk State he continued to be diligent and focused on becoming a teacher, and also discovered he was popular with young women and dated several before he selected Betty as his girlfriend.

After graduating on time, Vincent and Betty loaded her old car and moved across the nation to dry and brown Bakersfield in the Central Valley of California. She already had a teaching credential and job offer. Vincent did not. Like many new teachers, Betty worked long after school, preparing lesson plans for the following day, and worried about pleasing her students and administrators.

Hurry up and finish your credential so you can do more than substitute," she told Vincent.

"I'm studying quite a bit."

"You could take a heavier load."

"I'll have my credential in a year."

"Meanwhile, I'm paying most of the bills."

With the hand of a veteran grappler, he seized an arm, jerked her close, and said, "Don't disrespect me."

"What is it I'm supposed to respect?"

Vincent backhanded her mouth and threw her on the living room carpet. She held her bleeding face and looked at a man she'd never met.

"That better set you straight," he said, and stormed from their small apartment.

The police were interviewing Betty when Vincent returned. He was arrested and charged with domestic violence. She considered moving out immediately, but Vincent came home the next day and tearfully said, "I'm so sorry, I can't believe I did that. I'm going to plead guilty," and they spent the night making up.

The judge sentenced him to three years of probation and declared, "I don't want to see you in my court again."

"I guarantee you won't, Your Honor," Vincent said.

Betty and Vincent soon married, in 1988, and he finished coursework and became a dynamic and popular teacher in junior high school. At home the couple often quarreled, and Betty worried her irate husband might strike again. In two years they separated but Vincent wasn't lonely. He was already busy with Elaine.

"I want to marry you when my divorce is final," he told his new girlfriend.

Elaine wrapped her arms around his neck and said, "I love you."

"That's why I'm going to protect you from your family."

"What's wrong with my family?" she asked.

"They're trouble. I can see that."

Not long after Vincent became a single man, Elaine nuzzled him and said, "Time for us to get married. I'm pregnant."

"I just got out of a bad marriage and don't need another."

"We'd have a good marriage."

"I need my freedom."

"What about our baby?"

"We'll see," said Vincent.

When Margaret was born, Elaine warned him, "You've got to support the child."

"You two are breaking me." He abandoned them and often delayed payments for his daughter.

He didn't have time for domestic matters. He was teaching full-time and going to college at night to get his master's credential in administration. He knew he was going to run a school and needed a wife worthy of his talents. He searched energetically but without satisfaction until 1992 when he married a stylish lady who had a daughter.

"Tina, I want that girl to quit running her mouth when I tell her to do something."

"You give too many orders," his new wife said.

"I'm in charge."

"Not of my daughter," she said.

"You both better do what I say or else."

"Or else what?"

Vincent stepped close, almost standing on her toes, and shoved a long finger in her face. "I mean it."

Tina and her daughter moved out but Vincent made several gracious calls and the couple reunited until she got a restraining order, telling the judge, "My husband is verbally abusive, and I'm afraid he'll soon turn violent."

Vincent charmed her into one, two, and eventually three more reconciliations. He was just as persuasive at work. Every morning, now a vice principal, he stood at the school gate, waiting for poor kids from broken homes, and proudly looked at each before he offered a handshake. Later, in the halls, students congregated around Vincent, basking in the attention of an authoritative man who listened to their problems and offered encouragement and advice.

"I'm glad I'm divorcing Tina," Vincent told a male colleague in 1998. "She and her daughter 'disrespected my authority and tried to damage my reputation in the community,' but people know what I'm about."

"Damn right they do," said the teacher.

One weekday after school a smartly dressed woman entered the school office and Vincent, the only one present, thought how much he'd wanted to get to know Latin women.

"Hello there," he said.

"Hi. Can you tell me where the principals' meeting is being held today?"

"You're a principal?"

"Yes."

"Congratulations. I'm a mere vice principal. What's your secret?"

She smiled. "Lots of work."

"Where?"

"At an elementary school."

"The meeting's down the hall a few doors on the left, but I hope you'll stay here and talk to me, instead."

"I'd like to," she said. "We could meet in a restaurant after the meeting."

"Great. By the way, what's your name?"

"Reyna."

"Rey-nah, beautiful name for a pretty lady. I'm Vince."

They rendezvoused at a nice place they didn't notice much as they enchanted each other, sharing professional experiences and life histories and moving closer until their shoulders touched.

"I'm under your influence," said Vincent. "You better follow me to make sure I get home safe."

"You promise to be a gentleman?" Reyna asked.

"I certainly do."

Within seconds of entering Vincent's fine suburban house, they kissed in the foyer and fondled and undressed each other before rushing into the bedroom. After prolonged passion Vincent smiled and said, "I hope we didn't disturb the neighbors."

A romance ensued as they rode bicycles and exercised in gyms and dined and traveled in Southern California and on a perfect fall afternoon on the Santa Monica promenade he stroked her hand and said marry me and she replied yes, so he strode into a jewelry store and bought a gold engagement ring crowned with a diamond, and they hurried back to their motel.

Reyna often slept at Vincent's home but in a few weeks he started ignoring her calls and failed to respond to voice and written messages and didn't answer his door when she knocked.

"What's wrong, Vince?" she shouted through the door one night.

Vincent didn't respond. He wasn't home. He was out with Joanie Harper, a tall athletic woman who refereed basketball games and worked for the school district.

"You're the woman I've been looking for," he told Joanie.

"Treat me right and I'm yours," she said.

One Saturday night Reyna waited a long time in front of Vincent's house. When he arrived, she exited her car and approached to say, "What have you been doing? I thought you wanted to marry me."

"We can't talk here. Come on in."

A couple of hours later, heads resting on the same pillow, Reyna asked, "Do you care about me or not?"

"Of course I do. I'm just gun shy after two divorces."

A few months later Vincent and Joanie Harper had a son, Marques.

Reyna sensed something was wrong but still hurried to see Vincent whenever he called.

"Who's Joanie?" she asked.

"Just a lady I know."

"I heard you two have a child."

"No way. Who told you that?"

"More than one person."

"Easy, Reyna. You and I aren't married. It's better this way. Look at the divorce rate."

"Maybe I should start going out with other guys," she said.

"Go ahead."

"But Vince, that's my point. I don't want any man but you."

He saw Reyna and several other women whenever he wanted, but in 2000 Joanie told him, "We've already got a son, Vince, and I'm pregnant again. Why don't you settle down with me?"

"I'd love to," he said, thrilling her.

They married and she and Marques moved into Vincent's house.

"You're getting fat," he sometimes told her.

"I'll slim down after I have the baby."

"Then there'll be two kids I have to listen to and support."

After a month of increasing tension, Joanie returned to her childhood home, owned and occupied by her mother, Earnestine Harper, and in a few weeks Joanie welcomed her second child, Lyndsey. Vincent suddenly became a proud father and told Joanie, "I'll get us a beautiful home soon."

"That's wonderful," she said, praying he was sincere. "You know, our kids will be incredible athletes."

The young vice principal smiled tightly and wondered why he was taking on these responsibilities. He was more interested in his career and battling opponents on judo mats around Bakersfield and maintaining several extramarital affairs. In 2001 one of the ladies he called was Reyna.

"Hey, how've you been?"

"If you really want to know, try calling more often," she said.

"Come on over and let's catch up."

Reyna visited that night and before leaving in the morning she said, "Vince, I'm just asking you to tell the truth. Are you married to Joanie?"

"No, I'm not."

"And you don't have two children together?"

"I doubt those kids are mine," he said.

"I'm not always going to come over whenever you want."

"I hope we can be together."

"Then why are you married to Joanie?"

"We aren't married."

"Quit lying to me, Vince."

"Here, read this," he said, opening a file cabinet and pulling out a folder. "See. That marriage was annulled."

Reyna examined the document and tossed it onto the cabinet. "But you implied you'd never married Joanie."

"I should've married you. That's why I gave you the ring."

"Those two kids are yours, aren't they?"

"Probably."

"You could've told me," she said.

Vincent liked seeing Reyna until he didn't and again shut her out. In 2002 she visited his home and said, "This relationship isn't going anywhere, Vince. I can't see you anymore."

"I understand. It's my fault."

Cindy had been Joanie Harper's closest friend forever and had a key to the side door of the Harper family home facing busy P Street. In early 2003 they were sitting in the kitchen.

"Get rid of that guy, Joanie," Cindy said.

"I can't."

"Why the hell not?"

"I love him."

"Joanie, that's not love."

"I know how I feel about the father of my three kids."

"Three?"

"I'm pregnant."

"What are you going to do?"

"Vince is moving in with us next week."

A thunderous, "Oh, Lord," shook the walls as Joanie's mother Earnestine, a stocky community activist in her early seventies, entered the room. "I can't imagine that snake living with us."

"You want us to move somewhere else, Mom?"

"Why don't you move into that nice home of the vice principal?" Earnestine asked.

"He sold it," said Joanie.

"Why'd he do that?" Cindy asked.

"I guess he couldn't afford the mortgage," said Earnestine.

"He makes good money, Mom."

"Then why's he moving in here?" asked Earnestine.

"In two weeks, Vince and I are getting married."

"I'm certainly not going to the wedding," said her friend.

"You have to, Cindy."

"You're making a mistake, Joanie. I can't."

"What about you, Mom?"

"I'll be there, watching him."

After the wedding Vincent moved into the Harper home. In less than a month Earnestine told him, "You sure have a lot of late meetings."

"That's my duty as an administrator," Vincent said.

"I called the school last night. There was no meeting."

"Keepin' tabs on me again, Earnestine?"

"Damn right. And for such a bigshot, you aren't helping much with the bills."

"Keep your hands off my wallet," he said.

A few weeks later Earnestine told him, "Sure looks like you have less stuff here every day. You moving out?"

"Of course not," he said.

"I wish you were, but Joanie would be devastated."

"So would the kids," said Vincent. "Marques and Lyndsey love playing with their daddy on the front lawn. I chase them and then turn and run till I roll onto my back and let them jump in my arms. You must've heard Principal Carl Conway say hello from the schoolyard across P Street."

"I'm sure the principal's so impressed with the family man," said Earnestine, walking away.

Vincent bet he hated her more than she loathed him. Earnestine didn't matter. Neither did Joanie. After school the educator was concentrating on Leticia, another Latina.

"Why don't you come on over to my apartment?" he asked the teacher.

"I thought you lived with your wife and kids," she said.

"Not anymore. Got my own place."

She followed him there.

"Where's the furniture?" Leticia asked.

"I'll be getting some soon. I've already got most of my clothes here and everything I need in the kitchen."

"Where do you sleep?"

"Right there," said Vincent, pointing at the clean carpet before he kissed Leticia, who started visiting regularly.

Spring break was approaching and Joanie, eight months pregnant, said, "Let's spend lots of time with Marques and Lyndsey and get ready for our third child."

"I'd love to, but I've got to visit Melvin."

"Melvin?"

"My brother in Columbus. Haven't seen him in ten years or even met his wife and kids."

"You never talk about him. Why now?"

"I need a vacation."

Vincent parked at the Bakersfield airport and took a bus to LAX where he caught a flight to Ohio and in a rental car drove to Melvin's house and embraced his brother and said, "It's great seeing you. I can't believe how much we still look alike."

"Yeah, same height and weight."

"And the same hair," said Melvin's wife.

"We could be twins," Vincent said.

Melvin's three daughters watched as he said, "Almost."

A few days later, back in Bakersfield, Joanie asked Vince, "What's going on?"

"I'm just so busy all the time."

"You need to spend more time with your family."

"I played with the kids again today, and I gave you a bunch of money."

"Where's all your stuff, Vince?"

"We'll talk later. I've got a meeting."

Reyna was waiting for Vincent in a restaurant.

"Why'd you call me?" she asked.

"Because I care about you."

"Then why are you married and living with your wife?"

"We're separated."

Reyna shook her head.

"Really," said Vince. "Come on, let me show you my apartment."

They drove there separately. Inside, Vincent smiled, waving his hand at the barren living room, and said, "See."

"Vince…"

He embraced Reyna and started to lower her to the floor but she said, "Not here. Let's go to my house."

"Anywhere with you is the right place."

A few days later, in mid-May, Joanie Harper gave birth to Marshall. Vincent was present.

"Amazing," said Earnestine, "Vincent Brothers finally shows up for the birth of a child."

He glared but said nothing.

From her hospital bed, holding the baby, Joanie said, "You've got a wife and three kids, Vince, and it's your responsibility to take care of us."

He grabbed his wallet and slammed some cash on the table next to her.

"That's not supporting a family," she said. "I'm going to file for child support."

"I've withdrawn thousands from my bank account so I can help you and the kids. I've also gone to church with our family and fixed all kinds of things around the house."

"You do as little as possible."

"Show some respect, woman," said Vincent, storming out.

Earnestine pointed at the door and said, "Glad I made him give back the house keys."

A few times a week that spring Vincent visited to play in the front yard with Marcus and Sydney. Whenever Principal Carl Conway viewed the scene across P Street, he waved and said, "Those kids sure are giving you a good workout."

"That's the truth," said Vincent, grinning.

Vincent occasionally left more cash for Joanie but often departed abruptly on "business."

Among others, he was seeing Gina, a school bus driver who told him, I'm not a piece of meat.

"I know, baby. I really like you."

"When you're horny."

School was soon out and in late June 2003 Vincent told Joanie and her mother, "I'm going to visit Melvin for a week or so."

"What for?" said Earnestine. "You were just there."

"He's my brother."

"Always has been," said Earnestine. "How'd you survive ten years without him?"

"I've earned some time out of Bakersfield."

After Vincent left the Harper home, Earnestine turned to her daughter and said, "That man's evil."

"I'm praying he isn't, but I asked Cindy to be my cosigner at the bank. Just in case."

"This morning I made sure my pistol's loaded," Earnestine said.

"I doubt you'll need it, Mom. Besides, you think that old thing would work?"

"I'll get a new one pretty soon."

Vincent parked at the Bakersfield airport on Wednesday July second and took a bus to LAX and boarded a flight to Columbus where he drove a rental car to Melvin's house and dined with his relatives before spending the night. In the morning of July third, he handed Melvin his credit card.

"What's this for?" asked his brother.

"Go on out and buy some things the next few days."

"I'll pay you back."

"No way," said Vincent. "I appreciate your hospitality. I'll be sleeping here every night and sightseeing during the day. Let's watch the fireworks tomorrow."

"Okay," said Melvin.

Early on the morning of Thursday July fourth Vincent placed his phone on a bedside table in the guest bedroom, tiptoed to the hall bathroom and soaked towels and hung them by the shower. Then he carried a small bag of essentials, including sandwiches and snacks, quietly exited through the front door, and walked to his rental car. He wasn't going sightseeing. He was heading west, trying to cover more than two thousand two hundred miles. He prayed he wouldn't get sleepy and imagined a race car driver rushing across the plains and desert for a special purpose. He made quick stops for gas and bathroom breaks. He knew he had to be careful. He couldn't go anywhere that might have cameras. He slowed but pulled away from several suspicious places. He didn't speak except to conduct business. He paid cash and hurried away.

He had to get to Bakersfield but not too soon and needed to slow down. He couldn't arrive before Sunday morning July sixth. Where would he stay? What if someone spotted the popular educator? He slept a little at a rest stop in the desert and timed it just right and, after putting on a baseball cap, pulled into Bakersfield with plenty of gas when Joanie, Earnestine, and the two kids were at church. Oh god. How could he have forgotten six-week-old Marshall? He'd never been to church. Joanie had been talking about taking him. But what if he was still home with a babysitter? Vincent was a gambler. He bet the baby was at church with the other four.

Arriving at the Harper house, Vincent thought, "Old witch took my keys but not before I had duplicates made. I've also got the spare garage door opener. Come on, baby, please." He pushed the opener and the door rose smoothly and he drove inside and immediately closed the door and stepped out of the car. He was excited and horrified and sick as he put a key in the utility room door and entered the Harper house and walked into the recreation room to the sliding glass door leading to the patio and backyard. He removed the long rod at the base of the glass door and then unlocked and pulled it open a little and peered through the sliding barred door to make sure no one was looking over the fence. He'd probably have to kill anyone threatening the whole operation. Vincent thought he was undetected when he unlocked the heavy barred door and then closed the glass door, leaving it unlocked, before he departed.

Joanie Harper was happy at church with Earnestine and the kids, and all their friends and fellow worshipers were excited to see baby Marshall begin his spiritual life this day. Video cameras rolled. Hugs and kind words abounded. Joanie and Earnestine also gave thanks for the health of Marques and Lyndsey, ages four and two. Joanie told her mom, "This is our family's best day ever."

After the service, the Harpers dined in a restaurant and arrived home before two p.m. and prepared to return to church for another service at six o'clock. They needed a nap. Earnestine retired to her bedroom near the front of the house. Joanie's bedroom was in the rear, next to the recreation room and opposite the sliding doors. She undressed and hung her clothes in the closet and folded Marques' clothes and put them on a chair by the bed. He lay next to Lyndsey who was wearing the same outfit from church. Joanie changed Marshall's diaper and the four relaxed in Joanie's big bed and were soon asleep.

Vincent Brothers, after nervously driving around east Bakersfield, parked his rental car near the Harper's house on P Street and, still looking for witnesses he might have to eliminate, opened the backyard gate and crept to the heavy barred door and slowly pulled it open a couple of feet before he quietly opened the sliding glass door and stepped through and closed both doors. Did he hear something? Did someone hear him? It didn't matter now. He squeezed a .22 caliber pistol and sprinted through the recreation room into Joanie's bedroom and shot her in the head and shot her in the head again and shot her in the head again and fired two shots into her arm and another bullet into Lyndsey's back. Terrified, Marques looked at his father and bit fingers from one hand to the bone, splattering blood on his lips.

"Joanie, Joanie, what in God's name's going on back there?" Earnestine shouted.

Vincent dashed out of the bedroom and through the recreation room and an interior sliding glass door to an unoccupied room and turned hard left into the hall where Earnestine was aiming her old pistol at him but it failed to fire and he twice shot her in the face and rushed back to Joanie's bedroom and placed his pistol on Marques' forehead and fired a single shot and then shot little Marshall in the back and dashed into the kitchen to grab a knife and stormed back to the bedroom and several times stabbed Joanie's lifeless body. Then the educator lifted a large television from its stand and set it on the floor and moved a computer tower but didn't take them or any jewelry or electronic equipment lying out or the hundred-dollar bill on a bedside table.

Vincent left his baseball cap on until he'd driven three hours out of town. He still faced two thousand miles back to Columbus. This trip was going to be harder. He had less adrenaline and more tension and was crying and resentful that the Harpers put so much pressure on him. He reminded himself to keep an eye out for police looking for speeders. But they couldn't be looking for him, could they?

At church Sunday evening, Joanie's friend Cindy wasn't concerned that the Harpers didn't return for the service. She figured Marshall and the family were relaxing at home. On Monday, however, Cindy worried when no one answered her numerous calls to the Harpers and by Tuesday morning July eighth endless ringing unnerved her and she drove to their house and inserted her key in the side door on P Street but couldn't push it open more than two inches through which she saw wires crawling out of the television and feared the Harpers had been robbed. She ran to the front door, but it required another key and was locked. Of course it was. The Harpers always locked their doors and windows. She hurried into the backyard and faced the heavy barred door guarding the sliding glass door, thinking no way either of these would be unlocked but tried the barred door and pulled it open and then was frightened to find the sliding glass door also unlocked. She walked uneasily in and called, "Joanie, Joanie," and stepped through the recreation room and into her friend's bedroom and saw purple toes and feet on the bed next to dead children and screamed, "Oh dear God," and called nine-one-one.

Vincent, armpits sweating despite the air conditioner, drove hard the rest of Sunday and all of Monday save for a short rest that night and early Tuesday July eighth arrived at Melvin's home in Columbus and tiptoed to the guest bedroom and writhed in bed. In a few hours he got up and showered the first time in four days. Grinning like a crazed cat, he walked out of the bedroom and said, "Hey, there, how you doin'?"

"Great," says Melvin. "Geez, Vince, what the hell's wrong with you?"

A frown enveloped Vincent's face, and he said, "There's nothing wrong with me. I'm fresh and relaxed. Is that clear?"

"Sure, Vince, no problem."

They ate breakfast, Melvin's wife and three daughters glancing at their visitor before looking back at Melvin. The brothers needed a good meal. They were going to drive eleven hours to visit their mother in North Carolina. Vincent, Melvin, and Mrs. Brothers were talking when the phone rang. Elaine, mother of Margaret, Vincent's oldest and only surviving child, told her, "They're dead, all of them."

"Who, sweetheart?" asked Mrs. Brothers, and when told she shouted, "Vincent, get in here and talk to Elaine."

Despite the phone being at her side, she heard Elaine say, "No, I won't talk to him."

"What happened, Mom?" Vincent asked and ran to grab a phone offering only dial tone.

"All five are dead," she said.

"Who?"

"Your family."

He thrust the phone back to her and, fists clenched and face pointed down, staggered to the sofa and shoved his face into cushions as he cried.

In Bakersfield police quickly gathered information about Vincent and in two days flew to North Carolina. Vincent, as instructed, met them at the local police station. Detective Mike Hargrove, a native of hardscrabble Kern County, sat directly across a long table from Vincent. Another Bakersfield detective and two locals sat around Hargrove and

Brothers, listening.

"You say you were in Columbus, staying with your brother Melvin?" Hargrove asked.

"Yes, sir."

"Were you with him Saturday July fifth?"

"Saturday I was with another brother, Troy."

"Where can we find Troy?" Hargrove asked.

"Troy's kind of a nervous person. I don't know where he is right now. But I'll try to find out."

"What about Sunday July sixth? Who were you with?"

"I was driving around alone that day."

Hargrove turned to his Kern County colleague and said, "We've got to interview both brothers."

"When?" asked the detective.

"Soon as we're done here."

"Just a minute, sir," said Vincent. "We're quite finished here. I demand an attorney."

The detectives glanced at each other, and one of the locals said, "Sure. We've got lots of good attorneys around here."

"I want an attorney from Bakersfield to protect my rights."

Vincent and the others stood. The next day, accompanied by his attorney, he was arrested as a person of interest and held several hours until the aggrieved educator and his attorney gained his release and he returned to his barren apartment in Bakersfield. He was a perverse and solitary presence at the family's four-casket funeral where baby Marshall was buried with his mother.

The school district promptly put Vincent on unpaid leave. He spent much time in his apartment and often looked out the window and saw police parked near his apartment. Some were uniformed in squad cars and others dressed as civilians in regular cars. When Vincent drove somewhere, they often followed. They believed he was planning to run. And in September he slipped away and again sped across desert and plains.

"Vince, what're you doing here?" Melvin asked. "You scared me."

"I just wanted to surprise my favorite brother. Nothing to worry about. How'd the police interrogation go?"

"Terrible. Like you told me, I said you'd been around the house from July fourth to seventh, but they kept calling me a liar and threatening to prosecute my ass and send me to prison as an accessory to murder."

"On what basis did they make those illegal threats?" Vincent asked.

"They've got a video of me using your credit card to buy stuff in Columbus on July sixth. Where'd you say you went that day?"

In April 2004, following months of tight surveillance, Bakersfield police arrested Vincent Brothers and held him without bail in Lerdo, the county jail. During three years there, he was visited almost eighty times by Gina, the ardent school bus driver, and more than that by Mark Taylor, his new attorney. Vincent enjoyed having visitors. Without them, alone in his dim cell, he sometimes wept that he'd never touch a woman again.

*　　*　　*

Trial began in April 2007 and the defendant faced adversaries including two former wives and several girlfriends and romantic acquaintances as well as Charles Jackson who testified he was drinking beers on his grandmother's porch, next to the Harper house, when he saw the defendant and said hello the night of July fourth, 2003.

"Several years ago, you had a head injury that still affects your memory, isn't that right, Mr. Johnson?" asked defense attorney Mark Taylor.

"My memory's fine, better than yours, I'd say. My name's Jackson."

"That was a minor error, Mr. Jackson. Your mental problems, according to your doctor, are rather severe and affect your ability to hold a job and function in society."

"I can function in this courtroom."

Mark Taylor stayed aggressive with other witnesses, frequently demanding mistrials that were dismissed by Judge Bill Franklin, and turned red when Lydell Rivers testified he'd been visiting a house behind the Harper's and that he saw Vincent in the backyard on Sunday afternoon July sixth, the day of the murders.

"Were you drinking?" Taylor asked.

"Yes," says Rivers.

"How much?"

"Three to five cans of malt liquor, twelve ounces each."

"That's strong stuff, twelve percent alcohol," said Taylor. "Maybe you had twice that many beers."

"Objection, Your Honor," said Susan Brown, the assistant district attorney in charge of this case. "That's speculative."

"Sustained."

"In three statements to police before the trial, Mr. Rivers, you never mentioned seeing Vincent Brothers," said Taylor. "Indeed, you only started talking while serving a six-week jail term for petty theft. After being released you were soon back in custody for drug possession, and then you tried to trade testimony for leniency and conveniently claimed you remembered hearing several gunshots Sunday afternoon July sixth."

"Objection, Your Honor," said Brown.

"Sustained," said Judge Franklin. "Do you have a question, Mr. Taylor?"

"Yes, Your Honor. Mr. Rivers, do your memories change according to your legal needs?"

"I know what I heard," he said.

The following week Mark Taylor smiled at Carl Conway, principal of the school across P Street from the Harper's house, and asked, "Mr. Conway, did you see Mr. Brothers playing with his children in their front yard this spring?"

"I sure did, many times."

"How did Mr. Brothers treat his children?"

"He was very kind and loving. I enjoyed watching them have a good time together."

Susan Brown declined to question Carl Conway. She thought he'd been duped but couldn't prove it and didn't want to badger a witness some jurors probably admired.

In two days Brown sensed a better prosecutorial opportunity. She was at her podium, squeezing a pen, her body tense as she studied a huge color photo of the victims. She turned to the witness stand and told Joanie Harper's best friend Cindy, "Look at the picture."

"I can't," Cindy said, crying into her hands. Vincent, meanwhile, pushed his face onto the defense's courtroom table and covered his head with strong hands and muscular arms.

"I said, 'Look at the pictures,'" Brown ordered.

"I told you, 'I can't.'"

"I'm not going to take this photo away until you look at it."

Brown stared at Cindy until she lifted her face and glanced at the photo before she resumed weeping into hands. Vincent kept his face on the table until Mark Taylor tapped him and said, "They took the picture away."

The following day Susan Brown called Melvin Brothers to the stand and asked, "Did you see Vincent Brothers on the Fourth of July?"

"I guess he was around."

"Yes or no?"

"I told you what I think."

"What did you do together on the holiday?"

"Just family stuff."

"Did you have fireworks?"

"I don't think so."

"Did you go anywhere?"

"I'm not sure. It's been a long time."

"What did you do the next two days, Saturday and Sunday July fifth and sixth?" asked Brown.

"Vince went somewhere with our brother, Troy."

"Where did they go?"

"It's better to ask Troy."

"I intend to," said Brown. "I'm just amazed you can't remember what you did at a family gathering on a major holiday."

"My memory's not that great."

"Do you remember using Vincent's credit card that weekend?"

"The police showed me the video of me using the card, so I guess I must have," said Melvin, who swiped a hand across his forehead and looked down.

"Please look at me when I'm questioning you, Mr. Brothers," said Brown.

"Okay, fine."

"Did you at any time see Vincent Brothers on Saturday and Sunday July fifth and sixth?"

"I thought I saw him when he and Troy returned, but I'm not sure. He must have been around, though. His cell phone was in his bedroom and wet towels were in his bathroom."

"That proves wet towels and an abandoned cell phone were on the premises. Nothing else."

Mark Taylor sprang to his feet and said, "Objection, Your Honor. The prosecutor is badgering the witness and ignoring critical evidence."

"Overruled," said the judge.

In a private attorney-client conference, Vincent Brothers asked Mark Taylor, "How do you think the trial's going?"

Taylor exhaled.

"I know I don't have to testify, but I want to," said Vincent.

"I don't recommend you take the stand."

"If I don't, I doubt this all-white jury will unanimously vote not guilty."

"A hung jury is probably the best you'd get," said the defense attorney.

"You think they'd try me again?"

"I know damn well they would."

"Let's do it," Vincent said. "I've got to get out of here."

Mark Taylor, who several times had asserted people both known and unknown to Joanie Harper and her mother and children might be responsible for their deaths, began gently asking Vincent about his murdered family, and the accused soon started crying and pushed a hand under his glasses to wipe tears from his eyes. He spoke so softly Judge Franklin said, "Speak up, please."

"I love my family and would never have harmed them," Vincent said. "And I couldn't have. I was far away in Columbus, Ohio, more than two thousand miles each way. I enjoyed visiting my relatives that weekend but wish they had better memories for times and dates and hadn't let the prosecution convince them they hadn't seen me for about three days. I definitely saw them on the morning of Friday July fourth and again that evening.

"The following day, Saturday July fifth, I got to spend time with my younger brother, Troy. We left Columbus early that day to see a basketball game in Bloomington, Indiana but later found out there was no game because the radio gave incorrect information. Next, we headed for the University of Missouri in Columbia and then drove to St. Louis to see the famous arch. We got back to Melvin's house in Columbus about two a.m. Sunday July sixth."

"Let me advise the court, Your Honor," said Mark Taylor, "that Troy Brothers is in this building and prepared to certify that Vincent Brothers was with him all day Saturday July fifth. What did you do the next day, Mr. Brothers?"

"I spent Sunday by myself. I went to Dayton to see some housing tracts that Troy recommended I check out. I also ate pizza and 'window shopped.' Back in Columbus I got lost and stopped to ask directions at a store made of bricks at Hague and Steele streets. At that point a boy crashed his bicycle into my car. An ambulance was called. I talked to the ambulance driver and offered my identification, but it wasn't needed as the boy was unhurt."

When Mark Taylor finished his questioning, Susan Brown stepped to the plate and started swinging. "Isn't it true that you were not the driver of the car?"

"I certainly was the driver."

"Isn't it true that you're lying about being there?"

"I was definitely there, and I even saw a girl nearby who reminded me of my daughter Margaret, who was then fourteen. I remember waving to the girl. So, I was right there in Columbus, Ohio on July sixth, 2003, when my family died in Bakersfield."

"That's another lie, Mr. Brothers," said Susan Brown, pointing to a man who in haste had just arrived in the courtroom. "Roger Tatum has provided written testimony about the accident and will also testify before this court. His car was the one hit by the boy on the bicycle, and indeed a police report was filed and the name on the report is Roger Tatum. That report was just placed on the prosecution's table. You weren't there, Mr. Brothers, so who told you about this bicycle accident? Was it a member of your legal team?"

"Objection," shouted Mark Taylor.

"Overruled," the judge stated, "and keep your voice at a civil tone."

"Who told you about the accident, Mr. Brothers?"

"I didn't need to be told. I saw it. I was there."

"So you expect this court to believe you instead of Roger Tatum and an official police report?"

"I certainly do."

Susan Brown glanced at the jurors. They were looking back and forth at her and Vincent, who scratched his cheek.

Questioning turned to the defendant's rental car and five thousand four hundred miles the rental company recorded were driven when the car was in his possession.

"That's an astonishing number of miles to be driven in such a short time," said Susan Brown.

"I did quite a bit of sightseeing," Vincent said.

"Not nearly enough to account for such a staggering mileage total. There's a better explanation than the one you've offered, Mr. Brothers. We contacted the Entomology Department at the University of California at Davis and asked them to examine the many insects in the grill of your rental car. The nation's foremost experts on Entomology certify that several bugs in the grill of your car are found only in the western United States. Your car was indisputably driven far west of any of the places you claim to have visited."

"Objection, Your Honor, objection," said Taylor.

"Overruled."

After another bruising day for the defense, Mark Taylor confidently called Troy Brothers to the stand.

An armed officer of the court reported, "Troy Brothers has disappeared."

"Your Honor, Troy Brothers is the only person we know who can account for all of Vincent Brothers' time on Saturday July fifth," said Taylor. "It's critical that we find him and compel him to testify."

"I agree," said Judge Franklin. "And I hereby order an arrest warrant for Troy Brothers."

Vincent took off his glasses, rubbed red eyes, and motioned for Mark Taylor. The attorney leaned near his client who whispered, "I know they were threatening to send Troy back to prison."

Taylor placed a hand on his client's shoulder. The trial was about over.

On May fifteenth, 2007, the jury found Vincent Brothers guilty of murdering his wife, his three youngest children, and his mother-in-law, and the judge ordered that he be sent back to his cell at the county jail to await sentencing. A few months later the judge ordered that he be incarcerated in San Quentin while he awaited execution.

"That was redneck Bakersfield," Vincent told an inmate in the next cell. "That's why the prosecutor portrayed me as a demon who has sex with more than one woman. I guess white guys don't do that. And when the only black was evicted from the jury, for saying he wouldn't convict, I was alone."

"What're you going to do now, Vince?" asked the man.

"I'll appeal and the prosecution will have to admit misconduct and I'll walk out of here a free man. Then my daughter, Margaret, will understand she shouldn't have come into court after sentencing and told everyone she was scared I might come after her and her mother and that she hopes I take a good look at her face because she's no longer my daughter and I'll never see her again until it's time for me to die."

The convict nodded but said nothing.

A generation after he murdered his family, Vincent Brothers still resides in a private cell six feet by ten behind a thick steel door dividing him from the polished brown hallway in Death Row at San Quentin. He sleeps on an iron bed and uses an iron toilet. After seven a.m. wakeup he daily joins several dozen other convicted murderers in the recreation yard overlooked by snipers. Three times a week he's locked in a shower for seven minutes. Back in his cell he often reads and watches TV. Prison officials report Vincent is a model prisoner who's patiently waiting to learn if his appeal to the California Supreme Court will lead to a new trial.

Alternative Interrogation

In Sacramento County Main Jail, I pull on a ski mask and approach the cell of Joe DeAngelo and nod to the jailer who opens the door. As I'd hoped, a bald and chubby old man is sleeping on his side, and I shine my flashlight in his face. Small eyes open to see my pistol in the beam.

"Don't move," I say. "Don't make any noise."

"Who are you?"

I holster my pistol and place the flashlight on the floor at the end of his bed and point to a long knife sheathed on my waist, and from my back pocket pull several precut rope ligatures and nod for the jailer, a woman in her thirties, to come help me.

"Turn onto your stomach, Joe," I say. "You know the routine."

He hesitates, and I grab his shoulder and pull him face down onto the thin mattress and then hand her the ligatures and she tightly ties Joe's hands behind his back and then binds his feet together.

"I need answers to all my questions, Joe."

"I want my lawyer," he protests.

"Dozens of your victims needed an armed attorney."

The jailer steps outside to retrieve my binder and tape recorder, hands them to me, and says, "I'll be watching nearby."

I stand over Joe DeAngelo, his left cheek pressed on the cot, and ask, "Were you abused as a kid?"

"No, I wasn't, punk. Were you?"

I squeeze my fist in front of his face and leave it there until he says, "Okay. I had a regular childhood, came from a good family. My dad was a gunner in World War II and flew in bombing operations all over Europe. I was born a little after the war."

"In Bath, New York."

"Right."

"And your mother?"

"Everyone called her Kay. She had my sister early in the war. I was the second, then she had another boy and girl."

"Four children."

"Right."

"Must've been difficult raising four kids after the war."

"No more than most families."

"But your parents divorced," I say.

"A few years later my mom took us to California. She worked as a waitress and met Jack Bosenko. He was a vet, like many guys in those days. They got married in Tulare. Then we moved to Auburn. Jack worked for a company that made cranes."

"How'd you and Jack get along?"

"He didn't treat me any worse than you. Why not let me sit up?"

"You never granted others that consideration." After pausing, I unsheathe my knife and cut the ligatures around his feet. He works one leg onto the floor and then the other and wobbles to his feet, turning to face me.

"How about my hands?"

"Sit down," I say, sheathing my knife.

He obeys.

"What was school like?"

"I was a good student, smarter than most of the others."

"You went to Folsom High School a couple of years but must have dropped out. I see you got a GED in 1964 rather than a regular diploma. Were you kicked out of school?"

"No."

"Why'd you quit?"

"I got a manual labor job so my stepfather would quit complaining about supporting me."

"Did he ever hit you?"

"No. I'd have kicked his ass."

"You could have?"

"By then, yeah. I was eighteen and ready to join the navy. I served two years as a damage control man on the USS Canberra over near Vietnam."

I look at the plump, weather-worn prisoner in orange garb, and say, "What happened after the service?"

"I was ambitious. I went to Sierra College in Rocklin for two years and got good grades."

"You also had a girlfriend."

"So what?"

I open my binder and say, "Why so defensive? Must've been quite a romance. Look at this article in the Auburn Journal announcing your engagement."

"Called it off."

"Who called it off? You or Bonnie?"

"We called it off."

"Are you sure? In a little while Bonnie married a young man who went on to become a wealthy accountant. Looks like she made a good choice."

"Screw you."

"Why did Bonnie break up with you?"

"I'm not talking about her anymore."

"We'll move on, for now."

Joe's turning red.

"Relax. Next, you attended Sacramento State and graduated in just two more years. Pretty good."

"I studied criminal justice, wanted to be a top cop."

"And you met Sharon Huddle at school."

"You've been reading."

"Mainly superficial stuff."

"Which is getting too damn personal."

"Settle down, and look at this, another article about you in the Auburn Journal, this one announcing your 1973 marriage to Sharon Huddle at a church in Auburn. Seems like you knew how to get girlfriends."

"I did okay. I was a decent looking guy."

"Then you took a job with the Exeter Police Department, down in the Central Valley. Why Exeter?"

"My mother lived there."

"With your stepfather, Jack Bosenko?"

"Yeah, and my sister Becky and quite a few relatives."

"One cop who worked with you there said you were overqualified for the Exeter Police Department, being a college graduate, and he also said you were a know-it-all."

"I knew a helluva lot more than anyone else there."

I nod and say, "Great. Tell me about the Visalia Ransacker."

"I worked in Exeter, not Visalia."

"Only eleven miles from Visalia."

"Way out of our jurisdiction."

"You knew about him."

"Sure," Joe says.

"Were you the Visalia Ransacker?" I ask.

"No way."

"He seems like an early version of the East Area Rapist in Sacramento."

"That wasn't me, either."

"DNA says it was."

"I got nothing more to say until my lawyer gets here."

"Your lawyer ain't comin'. Got it?"

He grimaces and says, "All I know, the Visalia police said some wild guy kept breaking into homes, sometimes several a night. I suspected more than one man was involved. There are still burglaries in Visalia and everywhere else, you know."

"Yeah, but the Visalia Ransacker emptied closets and drawers, ignoring valuable stuff and instead taking a lot of things – photos, cheap jewelry, driver's licenses – that had sentimental value to the owners, and sometimes he'd drop those things off in the next places he hit. He also wore a ski mask and gloves. All that reminds me of the East Area Rapist."

"And a million other thieves," he says.

"And he'd usually leave himself more than one route of escape."

"Every smart thief does that."

I pause before asking, "Do you admire him?"

"No, I'd have busted him."

"Too bad you couldn't do that before he shot and killed Claude Snelling, the professor from College of Sequoias."

"Damn right."

"The Ransacker was trying to kidnap Snelling's daughter."

"Terrible. I've got three daughters."

"You didn't have any daughters then," I say. "The murder took place in 1975. A few months later, the Ransacker stopped. Most authorities think he got out of town. Maybe to Auburn."

"There's no proof of that."

"Okay, who knows where the Ransacker went? We do know Joe DeAngelo, who sits before me, joined the Auburn Police Department in 1976."

"That's right."

"The rapes in east Sacramento began in June that year."

"Every city has plenty of rapes."

"Not with this M.O. Before he attacked, this guy prowled and peeped, and called and hung up, and sometimes broke in first to learn the layout of the house. He prepared himself to get away with a break-in and rape in June, July, August, and September, and four in October, and another in November, and another in December, and two in January 1977, and another in February, and two more in March, and all the attacks were on the east side: Rancho Cordova, Del Dayo, back to Ranch Cordova, twice in Citrus Heights, where you lived until a week ago, then twice more in Del Dayo, and back to Rancho Cordova and Citrus Heights, then nearby Carmichael, and twice back to Citrus Heights. About this time, people started fearing the East Area Rapist."

"I didn't live in any of those places in 1977. I lived in Auburn, thirty miles east of Sacramento, and I busted criminals. I wasn't one of them."

"What was your address?"

"Don't remember."

"They'll find out where you lived then. Maybe Sharon Huddle will answer that for us."

"Wives can't testify against their husbands."

"I thought you got divorced around 1991."

"We're just estranged."

"While he prowled, the rapist often stood in flower beds or walked trails and greenbelts behind homes, and he left some nice footprints, size nine. What size shoe do you wear?"

"Same size as you," Joe says.

"By March 1977 the East Area Rapist had struck fifteen times and most victims felt he knew his way around and who'd be home and where they'd be sleeping. He got off on waking them with a flashlight and showing them his gun."

Joe says, "Did you get off tonight?"

"No, and I don't understand anyone who would. This guy also enjoyed tying them up with ligatures of string or rope or ripped towels and ransacking their houses and eating and drinking whatever he wanted from the refrigerators. He had a great time. Or did he? The women he preyed on couldn't see his masked face, but they felt his tiny penis when he made them masturbate him before the rapes. I'm sure you know, a judge just ruled the police can take photos of what you've got."

Joe doesn't respond. He stares at the drab wall behind me.

"After that fifteenth rape, the media reported you had only attacked women."

"I didn't attack anyone."

"Fine, the East Area Rapist had only attacked women and girls. Then he started attacking couples. He must've craved more risk. A lot of guys could've beaten him up or shot him. I wish just one guy had been armed and ready."

I reach into my binder and hold up a list. "Look at these times, almost always after one a.m. and usually after two or three. When he woke them, he'd hiss through clenched teach, 'Be quiet, or I'll kill you. Tie up your husband.' And you would – excuse me, he would – throw the ligatures onto the bed. Then he'd tie the woman up and retie her husband's hands and feet and put dishes on his back and say, "If I hear anything, I'll kill you both.' He loved that phrase. Probably still does.

"Imagine what those husbands were thinking when the rapist left them bound and helpless face down on beds as he led their wives into living rooms where he'd already silenced the place by turning off heaters and air conditioners. He needed to hear inside and outside, and he had to see the invariably attractive women he'd come for. Not their bodies beneath his but the fearful eyes and expressions softly lit by silent TVs covered with towels."

Joe DeAngelo scowls at me.

"This guy had a knack for finding lotions," I say. "Guess having it rubbed on by hands bound behind backs turned him on. No matter how aroused he got, though, he still had less than the men he'd bound in those bedrooms. 'Am I good?' he'd ask. 'Am I good?' Nonresponders were slapped and threatened and cursed. One woman told him, 'Oh yeah, you're great,' and the rapist pulled up and said, "Really? That's not what I usually hear.'

"He knew she was bluffing. It didn't matter what any of them said. He was in charge. His gun and knife and ligatures made sure of that. The newly empowered man was now free to raid the refrigerator. That reminds me, guys on the Auburn police force called you 'Junk Food Joe.' Said you were always munching on chips, nuts, cookies, and drinking sodas."

"Me and lots of other guys," he says.

"I guess you've read the rapist shouted at one of his victims, prone on the living room floor, 'I hate you, Bonnie. I hate you.' You despised Bonnie after she broke your engagement, and your heart, didn't you?"

"No sir. I found another girlfriend right away and was soon a married man."

"The rapist on occasion cried for his 'mommy' and hyperventilated.

Evidently, he's very sensitive about his own feelings. He certainly knew how to be quiet. Couples often waited long after they knew he was gone and started to free themselves, but the guy would suddenly reappear and threaten them or simply breathe or touch them with his knife. Sometimes it was getting light. How did he keep getting away with it? The police concluded he lived fairly close and knew Sacramento well. After the twenty-second attack, in May 1977, he figured east Sacramento might know him too well, so he next assaulted a couple in south Sacramento.

"Then he took a few months off. In September he struck further south to rape a young housewife in Stockton. You ever been to Stockton, Joe?"

"Yeah. How 'bout you, smart guy?"

"Yes, but I hadn't been born in those days."

"They better investigate you for some recent crimes there," he says.

I slap the cot and say, "The East Area Rapist returned for several east Sac attacks, but in March 1978 he assaulted another woman in Stockton and, in a June frenzy, he struck five times, first in Modesto, eighty miles south of Sacramento, then Davis to the west, and back in Modesto, and back in Davis for two more rapes. A guy that mobile had to have some money. How did he maintain a job while traveling back and forth from east Sacramento, or Auburn, to those other towns? We were two years into the nightmare by July 1978, and people had been buying guns and floodlights and special locks and bigger dogs and staying up all night, and the rapist already had thirty-seven victims, female victims. We should also count the husbands, who sometimes were more traumatized than their wives, as well as children in the house, especially the thirteen-year-old he raped."

"He wouldn't have gotten away with that on my beat in Auburn."

"Right, you were still policing up in Auburn, and in October 1978 the rapist started attacking seventy miles to the southwest of Sacramento, in the East Bay. He hit in Concord, and Concord again, and San Ramon, and twice in San Jose, and Danville, and Fremont, then Walnut Creek, and twice more in Danville. Oh, during his East Bay rampage he struck a final time in Sacramento, in March 1979. I guess you know that. Right?"

"I know you're lucky my hands are bound."

"Makes for a more compliant witness, doesn't it? Here's what's really wild, Joe, and I think you know where I'm going. In June 1979 you were arrested in an east Sacramento hardware store for trying to steal a hammer and dog repellent."

He frowns.

"Why would a cop making decent money ruin himself by stealing cheap items from a store? It's crazy. And when the employees tied you to a chair, while the police were coming, you got emotional. Did you want Bonnie or your mommy?"

"Untie my hands…"

"If you really were just a regular Joe, I'd be sad you got fired from a good job that July and were convicted of shoplifting in September. It's clear you completely lost control of your impulses."

He lumbers up and tries to kick me with his right foot and then his left. I move sideways, easily dodging Junk Food Joe, and shove him back onto the cot, cuffing his left shoulder with a right cross.

"I didn't enjoy that, but you're going to listen to what comes next," I say.

"You're a vigilante framing an innocent man."

"Where was your wife while all this was going on?" I ask.

"I was a hardworking cop, and my wife was in law school."

"Here's the stunner, Joe. That fall, right after your disgrace in Auburn, you moved to Goleta, or somewhere near Santa Barbara. Authorities think you worked as a handyman or something like that at a nearby shopping center."

"That's a lie. You can't prove that."

"I can prove you put your DNA inside Debra Manning in Goleta in December 1979. You envied her suave and wealthy boyfriend, Dr. Robert Offerman, didn't you? It appears he worked his hands loose from the bindings and tried to subdue you. You had to shoot him and Debra before you had your fun."

"Never happened."

"Really? I better spell it out: your DNA's also linked to the murders of Charlene and Lyman Smith in Ventura in March 1980. I guess you controlled them from the onset, and raped Charlene before you battered them with a log from the fireplace in their condominium. Several months later, you bludgeoned newlyweds Patrice and Keith Harrington in Dana Point, down in Orange County. You also raped Patrice, and your DNA's there, too.

"In these double homicides, all three women were pretty and their husbands or boyfriends handsome and affluent. Do guys like that make you jealous, Joe? Do sexy women turn you into an animal?"

"You can't deprive me of an attorney."

"I guess you were surprised when the next pretty lady, Manuela Witthuhn, was alone in her Irvine condominium. You probably wanted to kill her husband, too, but he was in the hospital. Police and others first suspected him. That was in February 1981. It chills me to note your wife was then two months pregnant with your first child. Later, in July, you entered the Goleta bedroom of Gregory Sanchez and Cheri Domingo, an athletic young man and his cute girlfriend."

"The hell I did."

I've got their picture on the first page of my binder section labeled photos. "Here, look at this guy, Joe. He'd have beaten your ass and killed you if you hadn't had a gun. I imagine he almost did, anyway, till you shot him in the cheek. That put him down, in the closet, and you struck his head a couple dozen times with a heavy object, the same one you used to kill Cheri after you raped her.

"How bad did he hurt you, Joe? Or was it more that he scared you? So far, it looks like you retired from crime to save yourself. Also, your daughter Maria was born a few months later. That may have restrained you for almost five years, until May 1986 in Orange County you raped beautiful teenager Janelle Cruz and almost tore her face off as you pummeled her with a pipe wrench or similar weapon. I don't get it, Joe. I really don't."

"All you do is talk and accuse."

"What happened?"

"Whatever it was, I wasn't there."

"Where were you, Joe?" I ask. "They'll find out, but right now there's a cold trail after the Auburn Police Department fired you in 1979 and when you reappeared in 1990 as a mechanic at Save Mart east of Sacramento."

"I was never absent from work and did a helluva job," he says. "Ask people who worked with me and the guy who ate lunch with me every day. We also fished together. Lots of people liked me."

"Fine, but what were you doing during those eleven missing years? Records indicate you've owned your current home, where they recently arrested you, since 1979. But you've sometimes rented it. Where did you live then? Authorities are developing information about your housing and even a gun purchase in Southern California. They want to know how you survived as the criminal later reviled as the Golden State Killer."

"I don't know anything about this," he says. "You've got the wrong guy, and I guarantee you're going to jail for this illegal interrogation."

"Pipe down, Joe. I'm not finished. I see your wife, Sharon Huddle, passed the bar examination in 1982 and later established a family law practice in Roseville. Other than your relapse, with Janelle Cruz in 1986, there isn't any DNA trail of you. It's again unsettling to note that when you mutilated Janelle, your wife was three months pregnant with your second daughter, Sandra. Your third daughter, Tanya, was born in May 1989. Such pretty names, Joe. Now they're young ladies, and Maria's a PhD candidate, Sandra's a physician, and Tanya's a graduate teaching assistant."

"Leave my family out of this," he demands.

"The public's interested only because of your behavior. They want to know if Maria and your granddaughter were in danger since they were living with you until DNA detectives converged online."

"DNA's bullshit."

"BS is when you're pushed into your arraignment in a wheelchair. You may be a better actor than most but not good enough to convince people a strong man of seventy-two has suddenly become an incoherent weakling. Plenty of your neighbors have recently seen you riding your motorcycle fast and mowing the lawn and fixing things in your garage. If they cut their lawns too early, they also heard you shout at them. The waitress at your favorite diner said your voice was fine two weeks ago when you complained about her service. And the police who arrested you say you were walking and talking fine. 'There's a roast in the oven,' you told them."

"Untie my hands."

"Do you think Sharon Huddle, whether or not you're divorced, is glad you're in jail? Is she surprised? Guess that's two questions. Really, I've got thousands. She was married to you at least eighteen years and knows more than anyone but you. It's surprising you didn't try to be nicer instead of going over to her house, ringing the doorbell to bring her outside, and engaging in what neighbors call 'epic shouting matches…in a toxic marriage.' Evidently, she never let you inside. That was a good decision."

I unsheathe my knife and say, "Stand up and turn around, Joe."

He doesn't budge. "I said, 'Stand up.'"

After he slowly rises, I cut the ligatures binding his hands and motion for the jailer to open the cell door. She looks at Joe, but he avoids her eyes.

Breaking News: In June 2020, two years after his arrest, Joe DeAngelo pleaded guilty to thirteen murders and thirteen rapes and confessed to dozens of other sexual assaults. Two months later, DeAngelo faced many of his victims and their families in Sacramento Superior Court. They called him "subhuman" and "a sick monster" and described some of the horrors portrayed above. Following four days of courtroom confrontation, Joe DeAngelo was sentenced to life in prison.

COLD WARRIORS

The Slugger

In cold 1908 Wisconsin I was born tough and every year became more so especially at age fourteen when my parents made me quit school and go to work. I managed a chicken farm and pushed myself trying to get away fast, and when the business busted I ran a grocery and then moved when it did but knew this way I'd never become the first Catholic president of the United States so started high school at age twenty and in only one year, grinding around the clock, did four years academic work to graduate.

On to Marquette University I rushed to hit books while pounding nails, flipping eggs, and pumping gas. Despite a stutter I joined the debating team and overcame my problem by attacking opponents. I also starred on the boxing team: no matter how big the opponents I charged in swinging both hands, striking heads and bodies and anywhere else I could, and they were lucky I didn't follow advice an old Indian gave me, "The best way to beat a man is to kick him in the balls and keep kicking until you're kicking air where his balls used to be."

I never worried how hard I got hit or how bloody I was and knew punishment affirmed my guts and confidence, characteristics vital in my becoming an attorney in 1935 and then running for district attorney the following year and not despairing after the loss. In 1939 I ran for district judge and in speeches added seven years to my opponent's age.

"Joe, that's not right," said a campaign aide.

"Listen, he's an old man who's long fattened himself on public funds. He needs to be replaced."

Almost every day for three months I traveled icy Wisconsin roads to talk to people I backslapped and ate with, and then, privately to my secretary, I dictated names, addresses, and anecdotes she used in postcards on which she signed my name. This information we filed.

On my next visits I astonished voters, recalling, "Pete, I loved watching your brother play linebacker for the University of Wisconsin. Toughest guy on the team... How are your three daughters doing,

Mary? They must be in high school now, and I bet they're as pretty as you… Say, Jim, are you still in the real estate business. I may be looking for some land in this area."

Damn right I won and at age thirty-one became the youngest district judge in state history. As Judge Joseph McCarthy I didn't have to serve in the armed forces but in 1942 enlisted in the marines so I could defend my country. My superiors tried to protect me as an intelligence briefing officer for a dive bomber squadron but I demanded to go on some bombing missions and served as a tail gunner, blasting enemy planes. In 1944, still on duty in the Pacific and with only a few weeks leave, I ran in the Republican primary for the United States Senate but lost.

Since America was winning the war, I resigned my commission several months before the end and began planning my 1946 race for the Senate. During a rally in Madison, I charged, "The incumbent, Robert M. LaFollette Jr., didn't even fight in the war."

"He was already forty-six when the Japanese attacked Pearl Harbor," one his backers interrupted.

"The guy's yellow. On the other hand, I'm Tail Gunner Joe."

"I hear you didn't really do much fighting," the guy said.

"Plenty will tell you I did. You and everyone else should also know that LaFollette was a war profiteer who made thousands from investments. I sure didn't make that much. The good people of Wisconsin are sick of New Deal Progressives like LaFollette. He abandoned that sinking ship and is pretending to be a Republican though in fact he wants to turn this great nation into a communist nightmare."

Worried about my country, I hired many people to sign my name to seven hundred fifty thousand personal postcards that blanketed the state I crisscrossed in cars, buses, and planes to tell everyone, "That gentleman in Virginia seldom comes home except for fundraising and has for decades been isolated from us and immersed in the murky affairs of Washington, D.C."

After one of my speeches in Milwaukee, a friend of LaFollette approached me and said, "Senator LaFollette doesn't have a residence in Virginia."

"That's a technicality, since he's invisible around here," I said. "Besides, he must feel guilty about this issue since he rarely bothers to rebut me or even campaign. I know he's got delicate nerves. Maybe politics is too tough for him."

On primary election night I slipped into a bathroom for stiff drinks and later pumped my strong right hand to celebrate a white-knuckle victory.

In the general election campaign, I repeatedly attacked my opponent, Howard J. McMurray, asserting, "His mouth's a cannon for communist-infested organizations."

Most newspapers in Wisconsin agreed, and I won by landslide to become the youngest member of the United States Senate.

The press and public were excited to finally meet a virile, blue-eyed senator who gripped men's hands, escorted pretty and passionate young women to hundreds of parties and events, dated two Kennedy sisters, drank with thousands of people, and often shook dice in sweaty rooms, yelling, "Come on, baby, papa needs a new pairs of shoes," and then told staffers, "Thanks for the girl. I'll take care of her unless you find me a better one, and I'll probably give the lucky one ten bucks."

I didn't worry much about money. I knew more was coming because people wanted to help with loans and stock market advice, and they enjoyed hearing my latest political tips.

Plenty of senators envied my popularity and dynamism and ignored my warnings about communist conspiracies despite the Iron Curtain darkening Eastern Europe as the Russians devoured country after country, and developed the atomic bomb, and locked arms with the new communist dictators in China.

"Both Stalin and Mao have murdered millions of their own people," I declared. "Who can doubt they're plotting to annihilate us?"

In their next sinister step, the Russians planted an army of spies and operatives in our Department of State, Department of Defense, the armed forces, atomic bomb facilities, and many other vital areas including the media.

While most politicians postured or hid, I went to Wheeling, West Virginia in February 1950 for one of the most urgent speeches in this nation's history. Standing over the good citizens that night, I shook a paper and warned, "I have here in my hand a long list of names that were made known to Secretary of State Dean Acheson as being members of the Communist Party and who nevertheless are still working and shaping policy in the State Department…"

Within days I became hotter news than all the Republican senators who were trying to pigeonhole me, and to patriots among reporters I explained, "I can't give you the names of the fifty-seven card-carrying communists but am ready this very minute to read them over the phone to Acheson."

Predictably, he was too cowardly to call. And too many liberals in the press ignored communist conspiracies and, in some cases, were actually red. I vowed to save the nation, and J. Edgar Hoover supported me along with many other patriots. But new groups of cowards and traitors continually confronted me.

In the United States Senate, responding to those who didn't believe my speech in Wheeling, I lugged to the podium a briefcase crammed with documentation of eighty-one more communists who had infil- trated the State Department, and said, "These photostatic files have been given to me by concerned diplomats, and I'd like to turn this information over to you, and I will, in private, since I'll never betray my informants whose lives and careers would be destroyed if their names are revealed."

"Where's the proof?" several colleagues asked.

"Right here it is," I said, stepping to a table and spreading the papers. "It should all be obvious, and if it isn't by now it never will be, no matter how thoroughly I explain matters to you."

Fine, my colleagues decided to plant me in front of the Tydings Committee, led by Senator Millard Tydings, who scoffed, "After three days of our grilling, Joe McCarthy will never show his face in the Senate again."

Tydings, supposedly a hero in the trenches of World War I, and his Democratic conspirators browbeat and impugned me for four months before calling my charges a "fraud and a hoax…designed to confuse and divide the American people…to a degree far beyond the hopes of the communists themselves."

I counterpunched these and other enemies of American freedom, charging, "You're egg-sucking phony liberals prone to pitiful squealing that make you dupes of the Kremlin."

Truman, naturally, backed my enemies, but alarmed Americans hammered him in opinion polls, and in November 1950 Tydings, once considered a lock, lost his reelection bid in Maryland and, blessedly, retreated into retirement.

Americans wanted men who were ready to fight, and my popularity rose fast as Truman's sank. Donations poured in, especially after the arrest of Julius Rosenberg, a certifiable American communist who gave drawings and notes of our atomic bomb designs to the Russians. Liberal columnist and radio loudmouth Drew Pearson was another dangerous enemy, calling me a tax cheat and claiming I couldn't prove my charges. He persisted several times a week, forcing me to tell friends, "My most difficult choice is whether to kill or just maim him."

At a Washington, D.C. gala in December 1950, I genially told Pearson, "I'm going to tear you apart tomorrow in my speech to the Senate."

During dinner, sitting across from his wife, I said, "You'll divorce him once I prove he's a communist."

I downed plenty more drinks and later, in the bathroom, I twice kneed Pearson in the groin and said, "I demand you retract your lies about me."

As Pearson backed away and I stalked him, young Senator Richard Nixon rushed in and tried to push me away, saying, "Joe, Joe, come on, settle down," but I lunged at Pearson and flattened him with a punch to the head. Pearson struggled to his feet after the ten count, and Nixon, a passionate anti-communist, helped me find my car.

Despite the dangers of taking on the Drew Pearson smear machine, the following day, as a hangover battered my head, I told the Senate, "What happens to Joe McCarthy doesn't really matter. My duty is to expose Pearson as a degenerate liar with a twisted, perverted mentality that makes him protect subversive elements while acting as a Moscow-directed character assassin."

Truman, of course, was much more dangerous than any columnist, and so were Secretary of State Acheson and Secretary of Defense George Marshall, the World War Two hero who, along with the other two, had lost their balls and embraced treason and given away China to the communists and let the atomic bomb roll into Russian hands and blundered us to the brink of also losing Korea. Our great empire was about to fall. And, by God, fall we would if the nation didn't get rid of imbeciles and cowards like George Marshall and line up behind Joe McCarthy.

After he won the presidential election in 1952 and took office the following year, Dwight Eisenhower, another World War Two cardboard hero, didn't dare criticize me publicly. Neither did most senators, including the most influential, Lyndon Baines Johnson, and the most dynamic, John F. Kennedy, whose father Joe was a good buddy of mine. Jack knew his Catholic constituents in Massachusetts would hammer him if he undermined my efforts to save the country. The people of Wisconsin also understood my mission and reelected me with fifty-four percent of the vote, though my enemies gloated that other Republicans in Wisconsin won with sixty percent.

Everyone knew about Joe McCarthy, and most were comforted by my relentless efforts. Just as I took on big actors, writers, composers, directors, and other artistic scoundrels, I attacked little welders, clerks, and secretaries. I targeted every person and organization undermining the United States. I even blasted the Army.

"Do you have any milk?" I often asked aides. "Excuse me a second.

I'll just take it into the other room. Of course I won't put anything in it. I'm under intense pressure, and milk coats my stomach. Too many are suspicious of me but should instead be worried about powerful people who're comforting and protecting our enemies."

President Eisenhower wanted everyone to be happy and pretend a mortal threat didn't exist and refused to admit the raw reality that unless stopped the communists would continue to burrow into our nation. Anyone who couldn't see that was either an imbecile or a traitor. We had suffered twenty years of treason under Roosevelt and Truman, and, unless my unremitting efforts continued, I could see plenty more trouble coming.

In the United States Senate, as chairman of the most feared investigative committee in the world, I hounded generals to tell me names of those responsible for the catastrophic honorable discharge of an Army dentist who had once belonged to the left-wing American Labor Party. When a general claimed an "executive order prevents" him from providing details, I exploded, "It is ridiculous to the point of being ludicrous that an Army officer cannot tell the American people how many disloyal people he has gotten rid of. I may say that all the evidence of infiltration by communists and subversion of the Army has caused the Army to drop to a rather low point in the estimation of the American people."

In the coming days I had the duty to warn officers, "You're doggedly and deceitfully opposing my efforts to dig up traitors and spies. If you claim Eisenhower has ordered key files classified, you're a double-talker who lacks the brains of a five-year-old child and will regret it because I'll bring you back so Americans continue to see your disgraceful testimony."

The Army was edgy and challenged me to a battle starting April twenty-second, 1954, in the United States Senate. For several weeks before that I charged around the country and in front of aroused audiences declared, "I'm fighting for America now… (and) I'm going to finish this fight… Millions will see this on television."

I launched the Army-McCarthy hearings by proclaiming, "We must be vigilant day and night to ensure there are no communists teaching our children. That's a grinding task since a vast network of our teachers gets orders from Moscow. We must stop them because in the whole two thousand years of Christianity fewer people have been converted than in twenty years of communism. For our civilization, it is either victory or death."

Americans watched the showdown eight hours a day as I struggled to protect them. They appreciated my dignity when I informed Army counsel Joseph Welch, "I'm getting sick of being interrupted in the middle of sentences... Quit making this a circus and stick to issues... We have communist infiltration of every governmental agency. I have names. You, Mr. Welch, say that you want them before sundown. Since you have such a terror of where communists are located, I'll help... You've got a lawyer in your firm, Fred Fisher, who used to be a member of an organization that's a legal bulwark of the Communist Party. I'll give you all the information about that and won't even ask why you tried to foist red Fisher on this committee."

"Until this moment, I never really gauged your cruelty," Welch whined. "Little did I dream you could be so reckless. You've done enough. Have you no sense of decency at long last, Senator? I think all this hurts you, too."

I ignored the applause, and a fortnight later remained unfazed when Senator Stuart Symington preened for the camera while telling me, "The American people have had a look at you for six weeks. You're not fooling anyone."

"Prove members of your staff aren't subversive," I demanded. Symington got up and left. What a weakling. Democratic senators were cowards and, I soon learned, so were half the Republicans. In August 1954, they hauled me into the chamber and charged me with forty-six counts of misconduct. That was a farce, but they voted sixty-seven to twenty-two to censure me on two charges of, basically, being too tough on enemies. I didn't despair. I knew I could soon become president and asked allies to poll Republican leaders. Only three percent said they'd support me.

What the hell? I didn't need them. I just wanted another drink. Hold the milk. And give me another shot of morphine.

"Senator McCarthy, we know you're taking drugs, and we're not going to let this continue," a federal narcotics agent told me in private.

"I like the stuff and will find a way to get it."

The feds agreed and sometimes even helped me obtain what I needed.

I quit spending so much time at the Capitol and slept late and watched soap operas and ignored phone calls and friends who'd come over and say, "Joe, you're killing yourself. Get some help."

Actually, I didn't feel that bad. The hallucinations may have been tough, but I didn't remember most of them and was always well-sedated during hospitalizations. My young wife, Jean, cared for me there and at home. What a beautiful and supportive woman. In early 1957 we adopted a baby girl, and I told Jean, "It's a shame my liver's giving out. I'd have been a hell of a father."

Nixon Responds

My enemies said I was awkward and smirked at me. They were generally leftists and other cowards. Most wouldn't dare debate me. I'd have cut them up on the Whittier College stage. Academically, it was the same. I finished second in my class and third at Duke University School of Law. Despite that and exceptional public speaking, I was ignored by prestigious New York City firms. Their stupidity helped me enormously as I returned to California and practiced law and, as a respected but lonely bachelor, sought good fellowship by auditioning for a part in *The Dark Tower* at the Whittier community theater.

When this beautiful young lady with golden red hair gracefully entered the room, I knew at once. I was in love. But what should I do? I sometimes stared but didn't want her to catch me. A few times I tried to smile but she never seemed to notice. Maybe she'd glanced but wasn't interested. I couldn't accept that, especially since we'd all auditioned and were preparing to leave. What if one of us didn't make the team and I never saw her again? Well, I knew she'd make it. I heard someone say Patricia Ryan had appeared as an extra in a few films. But I might not get a part. As she almost reached the door, I rushed up to her and said, "Excuse me, ma'am, you may not believe this, but I'm going to marry you someday."

She froze a moment before hurrying out the door. Thank God I got a minor part in the play. Patricia was a costar, and the first night of rehearsal I told her, "You're quite an actress. I bet you're going to be a movie star."

"Oh no," she said, "I teach typing and stenography at the high school. I'm no longer trying to be an actress. What do you do?"

"I'm an attorney and quite interested in politics and history."

The next night she said, "I've asked around, Mr. Nixon, and everyone says you're an ambitious young man."

"Please, call me Dick."

"All right, Dick, if you call me Pat."

She got great reviews in the local paper, and even as an extra I was deemed competent but was most thrilled because Pat often laughed when we talked privately. Lots of people considered me too serious to be funny. Pat was different and wonderful, and I took her to restaurants and we danced in nightclubs and I sent her flowers and wrote poems just for her and before long I drove her to my parents' home nearby and on the way home she said, "You're going to be president someday."

"And I hope you'll soon be Mrs. Nixon."

She stopped smiling but didn't frown as she said, "I enjoy my independent life as a teacher. I certainly can't marry anyone at this point. In fact, Dick, I miss getting out of Whittier on weekends, which I'd been doing before we met."

"No problem. I'll take you anywhere you want to go."

"Please don't misunderstand. I still want to date other men. And I'm sure a popular man like you knows many women."

"Oh, yes, I do, but I'm only interested in you."

"I hope we can see each other as good friends."

"Sure," I said, "we can do that."

Every weekend, I learned from mutual friends, Pat went to the Los Angeles house of her sister and brother-in-law and was picked up there by handsome young men who drove cars nicer than mine. I didn't date much when she was away. I just sat at home, wondering what I should do.

In a few weeks I nervously dialed Pat and said, "I understand you're quite busy on weekends, but there's no reason I can't drive you to your sister's on Friday nights and pick you up there Sunday afternoons."

"All right," she said, and when we hung up I put a consoling hand on my forehead and wondered what I would've done if she'd said no. I hated weekends and the only pleasure I got was writing poems I gave Pat when I picked her up.

I needed to see her more and wrote another poem on a weeknight and decided to surprise her right away and knocked on her apartment door she opened and instead of smiling she said, "I have a headache and will soon be retiring. Do make sure you call in the future."

I kept calling and writing her and, thankfully, she stopped going to Los Angeles on weekends and we resumed dining and dancing and walking on beaches, and in less than two years I knew I wasn't the only one in love, and confidently asked, "Will you marry me?"

"Yes," she said, and we walked down the aisle in 1940 and moved into a small apartment we considered a wonderful home. Until the Japanese bombed Pearl Harbor, I couldn't have imagined leaving Pat's side.

"As a Quaker, I certainly qualify as a conscientious objector, but I can't stay home while millions of American men are fighting."

"I support you all the way," she said.

I wanted to join the navy and fight but got stuck in Iowa and asked my superiors to send me into the real war. They transferred me to the Pacific Theater, and I helped set up temporary bases for bombers on one island and got bombed every day for a month on another and was fired up to attack the powerful Japanese base on Rabaul but General Douglas MacArthur decided to leapfrog the island so, despite my efforts, I never got any real combat and was happy to return to duty near Washington, D.C. and receive two letters of commendation.

Pat soon got pregnant and our first daughter was born in 1946 and a month later I was released from active duty and stunned when a Republican committee member, who remembered my legal performances before the war, called from Whitter to tell me that he and his colleagues were looking for a House of Representatives candidate from our district, which also encompassed several nearby communities. I traveled across the country and arrived in full uniform for the interview. Afterward, they told me, "We'll let you know…"

I returned to Washington and waited three agonizing weeks before they called me at work and said, "We think you're ideal."

Fast as I dared I drove home and hugged Pat and told her, "Get ready for battle. We've got to beat that five-term New Deal incumbent, Jerry Voorhis."

"I knew they'd select you, Dick," she said, taking my hand and leading me to the sofa in our modest living room. "You're the most qualified man in politics."

I kissed her as she stroked my cheek and I said, "This is going to take every penny we've got."

"It's worth it."

"I think we can afford a little one-room campaign office."

"I know an experienced lady who'll type your letters, distribute campaign materials, and keep track of contributions and expenses," said Pat.

"Sounds ideal, but I couldn't pay her."

Smiling, she said, "All I need is room and board."

"You've got a deal. We'll host meetings in Republican homes all over the district, and I want you to give speeches, too."

"No, Dick, I'm not a public speaker, but I'll greet everyone and then socialize after your speeches."

"They'll love you."

This was a thrilling night and we talked about the campaign until the sun rose and we fell asleep.

Pat and Dick made a great team, and Jerry Voorhis got nervous and naively agreed to debate me, and I steamrolled him five times en route to becoming Congressman Nixon at age thirty-three. I energetically entered the Capitol and soon became a vocal member of the House Un-American Activities, defending the nation against communists, and many powerful people considered me an emerging star.

In 1950 I knew I could save California and my country from Congresswoman Helen Gahagan Douglas. Even her Democratic primary opponents for the Senate accused her of harboring communist sympathies, and one said, "She's pink right down to her underwear."

I simply approved of what others called Douglas – The Pink Lady. Most voters knew she didn't belong in the Senate. The nation needed a strong man with convictions. Mao Zedong had just seized China from Chang Kai-shek and the traitorous Truman administration. The

Russians had exploded their first atomic bomb. Spies were trying to pry more scientific secrets from us every day. Mao and Stalin then signed a mutual defense treaty. Senator Joseph McCarthy bravely began denouncing communist infiltration of the State Department, and I publicly stated, "God, give McCarthy the strength to carry on. Our very existence is imperiled."

What did Helen Gahagan Douglas offer, other than empathy for the enemy? Let me concede, she was a beautiful woman, a star of stage and opera and the best-dressed woman in public life. She should've stayed in show business instead of serving three terms in Congress and then, in the Senatorial campaign, gallivanting around California in a helicopter, avoiding me and the risk of even an impromptu debate. Instead, she both publicly and privately said, "Nixon's a pipsqueak… God help us all if he ever makes it to the White House. He's another Joe McCarthy."

I countered this dangerous woman by sending a leaflet titled "As One Democrat to Another" to almost seventy thousand registered Democratic voters. Identified as Congressman Nixon, I was pictured with my wife and two daughters, Patricia and Julie, at home in Whittier and also as a bare-chested noncombatant warrior in the South Pacific. Douglas and some members of the press were aghast. "He's not a Democrat," they shouted prior to labeling me Tricky Dicky.

Fine. Tricky Dick ran against The Pink Lady. Who was right? North Korean communists attacked South Korea in June 1950, and Chinese communists entered for the kill in September. That clarified what was at stake in the campaign, and a close race turned into a November rout and I became Senator Nixon, only thirty-seven and still rising. General Dwight D. Eisenhower knew I was a winner, and less than two years later he invited me to join his presidential campaign as a candidate for vice president, and I proudly accepted.

My enemies, fearing Eisenhower couldn't be beaten with me on the ticket, charged that I received eighteen thousand dollars from my supporters. That lie devastated me as many of Eisenhower's top advisers urged: dump Nixon. I demanded an opportunity to defend myself, and in September 1952 I wrote a speech and prepared to address the nation on television. An hour beforehand, Ike's people called and told me to offer my resignation at the end of the broadcast. They didn't know Nixon

From a Los Angeles set decorated like a home, I sat at a desk, Pat stone-faced and tense off camera to my left, and said, "Not one cent of that money ever went to me for personal use. Every penny was used for political expenses I didn't want charged to the taxpayers of our country… Pat and I don't have much but the pride that every dime was honestly earned… She may not have a mink coat but does own a respectable Republican cloth coat…

"And one other thing I have to reveal or they'll probably attack me for this, too. A man in Texas heard Pat mention our two daughters wanted a dog. And believe it or not, he sent us a cocker spaniel with black and white spots, and little Tricia named it Checkers, and the kids love the dog, and I say no matter what, we're gonna keep it."

Several minutes before my half-hour expired, I rose from my chair, stepped around the desk, and stood before the camera. Looking straight into the eyes of millions of Americans, I said, "Let me say this: I don't believe that I ought to quit the campaign because I'm not a quitter. And Pat's not a quitter… But the decision is not mine. I would never do anything to harm the possibility of Dwight Eisenhower becoming president of the United States. For that reason, I ask you to wire or write the Republican National committee whether you think I should stay or get off. I will abide by your decision.

"But just let me say… I'm going to continue to fight because I love this country and we're in danger… President Truman and Secretary of State Acheson have lost six hundred million Chinese to communists and more than a hundred thousand brave Americans to casualties in Korea, and they have permitted many traitors to infiltrate our State Department…. I'm going to campaign all over the nation until we drive the crooks and communists out of Washington. And remember, folks, Eisenhower is a great man… and a vote for him is a vote for what's good for America."

I knew I'd delivered a strong speech. But what would Eisenhower decide? What were his advisers telling him? That mattered less when Ike telegraphed, "Your presentation was magnificent."

The general nevertheless ordered me to fly to Wheeling, West Virginia where he would give a speech the next evening. I knew he planned to cross-examine me about other rumors and, quite possibly, throw me off the ticket. He sure wasn't going to do that tomorrow in Wheeling. After difficult consideration, I decided to fly to Missoula, Montana and continue campaigning. I wagered Ike wouldn't court-martial his political partner who had just performed heroically before sixty million patriotic Americans. You're damn right the old man kept me on the ticket and in November 1952 I was elected Vice President Nixon and thrust both hands overhead, flashing victory signs.

I soon realized I'd never had such a shitty job. The president treated me like a private in boot camp, ignoring my opinions on policy, if he heard them at all. And though Ike so often benefitted from my doing his grunt work, giving the tough speeches and trying to placate the most hostile opponents and "throwing myself in the mud so he could instead step on me," not once did he invite me to the private quarters of the White House. Who did he summon? Political nonentities, for the most part. People who couldn't do anything as well as Nixon, except socialize. That they did better, I suppose. But I didn't care about socializing. I only grieved about it, squirming as a man shy and uncomfortable in almost every personal setting. Should that matter?

It did to devious Eisenhower. Despite my tireless assistance, he wanted to dump me from the ticket in 1956. I knew he never liked me, and his wife Mamie never liked Pat or me. Ike had always been against me. This overrated general of course didn't have the guts to tell me. He instead sent a political operative with the dagger. Fortunately, this shrewd Republican conducted private polls that proved none of the stiffs Ike was considering even registered against me. He had to accept he needed Nixon in his rematch against Adlai Stevenson, but I knew he resented his weakness.

After we won, my obscurity continued except during foreign policy assignments like the trip to South America where Pat and I and our small security detail barely escaped violent anti-American protestors. During my visit to Moscow, Soviet Premier Nikita Khruschev and I visited the exhibition of a "typical American home" equipped with a refrigerator and dishwasher in the kitchen and a washer and dryer in the utility room.

"These capitalist luxuries mean nothing," Khruschev said, waving his hand at the kitchen.

"In fact," I said, "these built-in appliances make the lives of our housewives much more convenient."

"We don't care about such things for the present. We're building for the future, and in several years we will bury you. Your grandchildren will live under communism."

"On the contrary, your grandchildren will live as free people."

"We'll determine our future," he said. "Your country is much older than ours, but we already have bigger and more powerful missiles."

"In the nuclear age, we would both lose a war," I reminded him.

Khruschev admired my insights and toughness, and so did the American public, which saw a film of this exchange on television. The Russians, as I insisted, also watched the telecast.

By 1960 I was clearly the best presidential candidate and ready to become the most powerful man on earth but had to watch those around me. I warned and lectured aides and volunteers, "Don't send out important press releases unless I've personally checked them… Don't ever let a bunch of goddamn leftist hecklers make me look bad in public again… You're not going to ruin Nixon… I don't need a campaign manager. I know more about politics than any man alive… It's obvious I can only trust myself…"

Following the Republican primary, I delivered an eloquent acceptance speech at the convention and shot to a big lead, and John

F. Kennedy, my Democratic opponent, began to attack not only me but the old man, calling our country weaker than before the Eisenhower administration. Ike couldn't handle the abuse, so he sent word he wanted to counter Kennedy and campaign for me down the stretch. I didn't invite him to do so.

"The president is insulted you won't accept his help," his minions told me. "You need him."

I let Ike stew before I arranged a private meeting and told him, "Mr. President, you've already done enough."

Campaigning hard eighteen hours and more every day, I needed to slow down and rest a little but couldn't and, rushing to my next speech, lost balance getting into a limousine and banged my knee on the door.

"Are you all right, sir?" asked the chauffeur.

"Oh, sure," I said, rubbing a rapidly swelling wound through my pants. "I took hundreds of harder hits on my college football team."

"You played in college?"

"I didn't actually play in games but made it to every practice."

I never had an injury nearly this bad in football. My knee ached constantly and kept getting worse and I had to lie in bed two weeks, regularly getting painful shots of antibiotics under my kneecap. During this layoff I missed scheduled campaign appearances in seven states.

"Dick, you're not in condition to make it to all fifty states," Pat said.

"I promised I would."

"It's all right. People understand you're injured and bedridden."

"Don't say I'm bedridden, Pat. You think Americans would elect a president who couldn't get out of bed after a little injury."

"It's serious, Dick. You've lost twenty pounds."

"I'll just tighten my damn belt."

Several aides told me, "Mr. Vice President, you're already leading by a few points in the polls. Maybe it's better to cancel the debates."

"I can't do that. The voters would think I'm a coward. I want Jack Kennedy up there on that stage with me. He's everything most Americans should hate: a rich kid who's never really worked, an elitist liberal, an unfaithful husband, and a lazy and undistinguished legislator."

Back on the campaign trail I pushed myself, flying and riding and zigzagging all over the country to shake hands and give speeches. While getting only a few hours of sleep a night, I also prepared for the first debate. My advisers pestered me about the lighting and photographic needs of television until I explained, "I'm the preeminent user of television in political history."

I banished the irritating guy who was supposed to be my TV expert. Finally, on the afternoon of the debate, I let him see me for a half-hour.

"Mr. Vice President," he said, "you look a little pale and haggard. That's not good for television."

"Hold it right there, fellow. Did my aides tell you to say that?"

"No, sir, that's my professional opinion. But don't worry. We'll cover most of that with makeup."

"My enemies would call me effeminate."

"This is the same makeup John Wayne wears."

"Not a chance."

Even though I was sweating rivers down my forehead and temples and wetting my upper lip, in an oven-hot room, I knew I out-thought and out-talked Kennedy, whose bootlegging father couldn't buy his little boy out of this one.

Afterward I was exultant and told my aides, "I think I won the presidency tonight."

They stood taut and silent and a few even called the debate a "disaster."

"I disagree."

"Will you please wear makeup the next three debates?" asked someone in the group. I was too tired to remember who.

"Okay, okay," I said.

I didn't think I'd looked bad the first debate but certainly looked better in the others and made sure studio temperatures were cool as I shellacked Kennedy. Shockingly, the polls indicated my lead had become a deficit of four or five points. I guess the TV audience was more impressed by a condescending pretty boy than a man who'd mastered the issues. I responded with an even more intense campaign schedule, and Eisenhower made some helpful appearances, too.

As polls tightened, Pat and I drove ourselves in the final days and confidently cast our ballots on election morning in Whittier. That evening in Los Angeles we sat in our suite at the Ambassador Hotel, watching the returns crawl in. It was agonizingly close. I'd win a state and Kennedy would win two and I'd take two and he'd win one and this trend continued, back and forth. The biased liberal press had fallen in love with my opponent and praised him all the time, otherwise I'd have been far ahead. Late that night the popular vote stood about even, Kennedy leading by two-tiny-tenths of one percent out of almost seventy million votes, but we lagged in the Electoral College. Maybe I should have let Ike campaign for me a little more and certainly should've monitored the behavior of Kennedy's running mate Lyndon Johnson, known as Landslide Lyndon, and of shifty Chicago Mayor Richard Daley.

"Dick, we keep hearing of irregularities at the polls," Pat said. "They're stealing Texas and Illinois from you."

"They're despicable," I said, "but there's nothing we can do."

"Challenge them," she said. "Tell the nation the truth."

"The Electoral Colleague numbers simply can't be overcome at this point, Pat."

"Demand a recount."

"That would tie up the new president for several months. I won't do that. It's time for us to go downstairs and concede."

"I'm not going," she said. "I won't stand there while you concede an election you won."

Stunned and saddened, I said, "If I have to go alone, Pat, I will."

I walked toward the door of our suite and was relieved my wife stepped up and took my arm and we walked out the door and down to a sad but thrilled crowd that clapped two minutes before I could speak. I didn't break down and neither did Pat. We knew we could relax a little and didn't need gray Washington, D.C. anymore. We were already thinking about sunny California.

We hired an architect to build us a beautiful home in Beverly Hills, but I had to tell enemies who accused Nixon of living in a palace, "I've only got four bedrooms and that's pretty doggone modest in our neighborhood."

I joined a friend's law firm and wrote newspaper columns and gave plenty of speeches to folks delighted to see a former vice president in person. Their chants and cheers reinvigorated me, and I told Pat, "People want me to run again."

"You just ran and almost killed us both."

"I thought we held up pretty well," I said, and poured a hearty drink, my second this early evening at home, and took a slug. "I know I can win."

"You can't beat Kennedy in 1964," Pat said.

I walked to her, put a tender hand on her shoulder, and said, "Relax, Pat, I'm not going to run against Kennedy. I'm going to beat Pat Brown in 1962. Don't betray me now."

"In case you're interested, Dick, I've got a headache and stomach-ache most of the time."

"I was born for politics. I've got to be in the arena."

"I'm not sure I can endure this marriage much longer."

"Are you threatening to divorce me?"

Looking meanly at me like she had that night long ago in Whittier when I stopped by her apartment without calling, she said, "I don't wish to be disturbed the rest of the evening," and marched away.

I thought she'd be thrilled to be married to the next governor of the nation's most beautiful and dynamic state. Governor Pat Brown couldn't compete with me. My speeches continued to generate momentum and in a few weeks Pat regained her energy and enthusiasm and at home said, "Come here, Dick," and took my hand before saying, "You know the girls and I will support you."

I needed their help. I faced more than a political opponent. I confronted reporters who weren't like guys in the old days, especially at the Los Angeles Times. They had raptly recorded my revelations about communist sympathizers. Now all the reporters and radio and TV guys bashed me and made Nixon the man more of an issue than Nixon the politician, and Pat Brown beat me by more than two million votes. And in my concession speech, I calmly – not hysterically, as many claimed – informed them, "You're going to be missing a great pleasure. You won't have Nixon to kick around anymore."

We were getting the hell out of California in 1963 and moving to the legal and financial capital of the world. Only in New York could I so quickly have gotten a job at a powerful law firm that happily changed its name to Nixon, Mudge, Rose, Guthrie, and Alexander. Politicians and financiers and their elegant wives began courting me, and Pat and I needed a luxurious place to entertain them and raise our two teenage daughters. We looked extensively before finding a promising albeit rundown ten-room cooperative on Fifth Avenue. Pat resolved to transform the place, and I vowed to avoid one of the building's other residents, Governor Nelson Rockefeller, who wanted what I yearned for.

"I've got to get back on the road," I told Pat.

"Why?"

"I'm a strategic thinker and can see what's developing."

"And what is that, Dick?"

"Kennedy's going to step on someone next year. In the meantime, I'll travel all over the nation, campaigning and fundraising for his opponent and as many Republican senators and congressmen as possible. I'll do the same in the 1966 mid-terms and beyond. By 1968 I should have enough goodwill and support to run again."

"For governor of New York?" she asked.

"Of course not. For president of the United States."

"Not again, Dick."

"Come on, let's have some drinks."

Tragically, President John F. Kennedy was assassinated in November 1963, and the following year I knew President Lyndon Johnson was going to trounce nuclear warrior Barry Goldwater, who scared people. I forced a smile and marched onto the Republican Convention stage and assured the faithful, "When Barry Goldwater gets through with Lyndon Johnson his theme song's going to be 'Home, Home on the Range.'"

My speech was a triumph, and many said, "If Nixon had been this relaxed and personable four years ago, he'd have won."

Before and after Goldwater's landslide loss I enjoyed flying around and giving speeches in forty states before enthused audiences who appreciated my help for their candidates and condemnation of our enemies. Nevertheless, I remained a patriot and was delighted to accept President Johnson's invitation to the White House in March 1966. After a secret service agent greeted me, I started to walk toward the Oval Office but the agent said, "This way, Mr. Vice President."

Surprised, I asked, "Where are we going?"

"The president will receive you in his bedroom."

"You're kidding."

"No sir."

President Johnson, attired in pajamas at noon, greeted me near the door and enveloped my hand with his enormous right and said, "Dick, thanks for coming. Just make yourself comfortable in that chair."

He climbed into his Texas-size bed, took a few breaths as he studied me, and said, "Vietnam's a goddamn mess and I don't know what I'm gonna do. I've already got three hundred thousand soldiers there, and we're killing lots of the enemy and dropping plenty of bombs, but no matter what ass-kissing generals tell me, I know we aren't winning the war. And the American people get unhappier every time one of our boys comes home in a bag."

"Mr. President, forgive my frankness, but you're just not being tough enough. You need to send the right message. Drop more bombs on the bastards."

President Johnson and I continued our serious but amicable discussion for a half hour until Lady Bird, also wearing pajamas, entered the presidential bedroom. I stood and the smiling First Lady shook my hand and then stepped bedside and slipped in next to her husband.

"Thanks for coming, Dick," he said.

"You're quite welcome, Mr. President."

I continued traveling and speaking and Lyndon Johnson kept escalating and by 1968 more than half a million U.S. soldiers were in Vietnam.

In our fine Fifth Avenue home I told Pat, "He can't win in November."

"That doesn't mean you can, Dick."

I picked up my drink and tried to relax. "I need your support, not a devil's advocate."

"I'm not going to encourage you to run. I know the consequences. But if you can't control yourself, I'll help you, as I always have."

Every time I saw those goddamn kids – they were bums, really – rioting and throwing rocks and burning the American flag on television, I felt sorry for President Johnson. The poor man was broken and didn't know what to do. I did. I was a foreign policy specialist and people on the campaign trail respected that and boosted me to Republican primary wins in New Hampshire and other states, and one afternoon Pat rushed up, handed me a newspaper, and said, "Dick, have you seen this?"

"No, what is it?"

"President Johnson isn't going to seek reelection."

I didn't smile, I simply said, "I'll be damned."

Johnson had gotten modestly more votes in New Hampshire's Democratic primary than Senator Eugene McCarthy, the anti-war candidate, but fewer delegates. I sensed that Senator Robert F. Kennedy would soon start sniffing around, and my political instincts proved correct as he jumped into the Democratic primary.

"Do you think you can beat him in the general election?" asked Pat.

"Of course I can beat Bobby, by himself, but I'll have to run against the memory of his brother, too."

A few days later, following my speech, a reporter asked, "What's your response to the assassination of Martin Luther King?"

"When? Where?"

"In Memphis this afternoon," he said.

I thought carefully before saying, "That's an enormous tragedy. Dr. King's commitment to nonviolence greatly helped the cause of social justice in our country."

Campaigning in cities set afire by rioters, I said, "There's so much hatred and violence. We need someone to bring us together."

"Do you think the growing casualties in Vietnam are also part of the problem?" a reporter asked.

"I believe we must honorably end the war in Vietnam, and I'm the most qualified candidate to do so."

Week by week I noted that Bobby Kennedy was riding the wave of original peace candidate Eugene McCarthy and starting to win primaries and build momentum while McCarthy weakened. Unlike them, Vice President Hubert Humphrey couldn't run as an opponent of the war, and in fact bore Lyndon Johnson's Vietnam legacy like a chain around his neck. Neither he nor McCarthy could beat me. Among Republicans, I knew no one had the national base to challenge me. I would finally become the next president, if I could beat Bobby Kennedy.

Early in the morning of June fifth, 1968, I heard it on the radio. Senator Robert F. Kennedy had been shot right after his victory speech in the California Democratic primary. I set aside politics and prayed he would recover and a day later despaired when he died. I had respected Senator Kennedy, as I had his brother President Kennedy, and recalled recently having said, "Bobby and I have been sounding pretty much alike" in our advocacy of "economic empowerment for blacks."

"Dick, this isn't worth it," said Pat. "You could be next."

"I've got to take the risk because I'm the only man who can fix this country."

"If you survive."

We enjoyed a peaceful Republican Convention in Miami in early

August, and I was nominated to be the next president. I didn't see how the Democratic nominee, Hubert Humphrey, could win. Rioters at their Chicago convention in late August reminded the nation that my opponents had turned the United States into a cauldron of hatred incited by ignorant people who didn't understand our battle against communism in Vietnam.

"I have a plan to stop this war," I promised the nation.

"What's the plan?" shouted the doubters.

"I can't reveal the plan now or it wouldn't work when I become president."

President Johnson tried to rig the outcome when he stopped bombing North Vietnam shortly before the election, but he didn't fool the silent majority. On election night I huddled in my hotel headquarters with top campaign advisers and watched the count dribble in at midnight, one a.m., two a.m., three a.m. We cheered when the networks announced, "Chicago goes to Richard Nixon," and we watched and tabulated all night and by eight a.m. we knew I'd won.

From her room down the hotel hallway, Pat called and said, "I can't take this, Dick. I'm vomiting."

"Relax, Pat. We did it."

"Are we completely sure?" she asked.

"Yes, come on down here and kiss the president of the United States."

In my 1969 inaugural address, as Pat proudly looked at me, I stated, "The greatest honor history can bestow is the title of peacemaker." Sadly, the Johnson administration had left more than half a million of our troops in Vietnam and a few hundred were dying every week. As the new commander in chief, I had to protect our men as well as the people of South Vietnam. This I did in secret. We certainly couldn't tell the American people, and thus the enemy, about our plans to carpet bomb enemy military positions along the South Vietnamese-Cambodian border.

I still made this generous offer: "We are prepared to withdraw all American troops from South Vietnam if the North Vietnamese will do the same. Furthermore, we propose democratic elections in South Vietnam that would also include the Viet Cong. These elections would of course be internationally supervised."

Despite my having already withdrawn a hundred fifty thousand troops, North Vietnam responded by invading Cambodia in March 1970. Maintaining essential secrecy, I counterattacked the North Vietnamese in Cambodia. A few weeks later I appeared on television before our nation. After reviewing the enemy's behavior, I stood and eased to a beautiful map featuring light orange Cambodia and dark yellow Vietnam, and at numerous red areas along their border I pointed, in professorial style, and said, "For five years North Vietnam has occupied these sanctuaries all along the Cambodian border and up to twenty miles into Cambodia. These occupied areas contain major camps and bases, training sites, logistical facilities, weapons factories, and prisoner of war camps, and are used to launch hit and run attacks."

The silent majority understood my logic and declared overwhelming support, but the radicals continued to riot and threaten our internal security as well as our reputation abroad.

"Bob, I've got to take a nap," I told my chief of staff, H.R. Haldeman, on May fourth. "I'd like to sleep forever, but don't let me."

"Yes sir."

It was dark when Haldeman knocked to awaken me. I quickly dressed and walked into the hall, and he looked like a doctor obligated to convey a fatal diagnosis.

"What is it?" I asked.

"The National Guard shot and killed four students at Kent State today and wounded several others."

"I bet the students provoked them. Some were probably outside agitators."

"We don't have any indication of that at this time, Mr. President."

"Go find something that doesn't make this look like an execution."

"Yes sir, but I think you better prepare to speak to the nation."

Four endless days later, I confidently appeared on stage above a packed news conference.

"Mr. President, you recently called the war protestors bums," said a reporter. "What is your response now?"

"I didn't say all protestors are bums," I responded. "I was referring to the ones who threaten and attack innocent citizens, students, and professors. When people are throwing rocks at the National Guard, there's always a chance that things will escalate."

"What do you plan to do about problems that result from demonstrations?" asked another reporter.

"I saw the pictures of those four youngsters, and I vowed then that we would find more effective ways of dealing with protestors."

"Do you think it looks like we're headed toward a revolution?" asked a reporter.

"Not at all," I said. "We have freedom of speech. People can protest peacefully. We're not going to have a revolution. Revolution comes from repression. I have the same goals as those who protest. We want to end this war as soon as possible and bring our boys home."

I knocked every pitch out of the park that night and sure didn't want to sleep. I returned to my White House family quarters and called a few dozen people. Henry Kissinger, my national security adviser, and most others were also ecstatic. Then I made my most important call, to FBI Director J. Edgar Hoover.

"I've got Haldeman on this because I know there had to be some outside agitators," I said.

"I'm sorry, Mr. President, but I can't find any evidence of that."

"But you've only had four days to investigate."

"That's true," said Hoover.

"Keep looking. I know I've got enemies out there because the latest Gallup poll says fifty-eight percent believe the Kent State students were to blame and only eleven percent hold the National Guard responsible."

"I'll report to you as soon as possible, Mr. President."

J. Edgar Hoover couldn't find anything. He'd become old and undependable. What other agency could I trust? There weren't any.

Before long I'd have to build my own investigative team. That shouldn't have been necessary.

The media and protestors either didn't understand or were too dishonest to admit that Nixon was delivering exceptional results. I had put Americans on the moon and created the Environmental Protection Agency and peacefully ended school segregation and continued bringing our soldiers home, leaving three hundred thirty-four thousand and then a hundred fifty-seven thousand in 1971, and I vowed to keep making peace.

I'd long been working on what I believed would be my greatest achievement. I was going to visit China and diplomatically embrace its one billion isolated citizens. Twice I sent Henry Kissinger to prepare this historic event, and in February 1972 Pat and I and Kissinger and our staffs flew to Beijing where Premier Zhou Enlai greeted us and led the motorcade to our guest quarters. I was resting when Zhou, quite unexpectedly, called and said, "Chairman Mao would like to see you in his residence right away."

Never in my life so enthused, I called Kissinger. "Henry, I'm going to Mao's place this afternoon. Would you like to come along?"

He laughed. "Let me check my schedule, Mr. President. It appears that I can make it. What time?"

"Now," I said.

I was thrilled to see Mao standing to greet us but shocked how old and feeble he and Zhou looked. We moved to another room and sat in a semicircle, Zhou on the left, then the interpreter, Mao, Nixon, Kissinger, and his notetaking aide on the right. We praised each other's intellects and joked about Henry's zest for pretty young ladies before Mao shifted gears and said, "At the present time, the question of aggression from the United States or aggression from China is relatively small; that is, it could be said that this is not a major issue, because… a state of war does not exist between our two countries. You want to withdraw some of your troops (in Vietnam) back on your soil; ours do not go abroad…"

"I appreciate your viewpoints, Mr. Chairman," I said. "Since our nations don't want to dominate the world, we can find common ground, despite our differences, to build a world structure in which both can be safe to develop in our own way on our own roads... I also hope to discuss Taiwan, Vietnam, and Korea with Premier Zhou as well as you, Mr. Chairman."

"All those troublesome problems I don't want to get into very much," said Mao. "You can discuss them with Premier Zhou. I prefer to deal with philosophic questions."

"You're a very philosophical man," I said.

"And you as well," the chairman delighted me by saying, "Your book *The Six Crises* is rather good."

"You read too much, Mr. Chairman," I said.

"Not enough. I don't know much about the United States."

"We'll send you some teachers," I said.

"Please, history and geography teachers."

"That we will certainly do, Mr. Chairman," said Kissinger.

"Have we covered enough today?" Mao asked. "My health is poor."

"You certainly appear in good shape to me, Mr. Chairman," I said.

Stimulated by this historic meeting, we parted in good fellowship. In subsequent talks with Zhou Enlai, Kissinger and I stressed the importance of our two nations cooperating to contain the Soviet Union, which three years ago had engaged in a bloody border conflict with China, and someday normalizing relations and working together on a variety of economic and cultural initiatives. We also agreed that "all Chinese on either side of the Taiwan Strait maintain there is but one China" and that Taiwan could not be independent.

Before the trip, Pat had seemed tired and tense but in China she looked wonderful, especially in her long red coat, as she toured factories and schools and landmarks, shaking hands and smiling and asking questions in ways that charmed the Chinese.

I returned home a hero and believed I would become one of history's greatest peacemakers if I succeeded during my upcoming trip to the Soviet Union, and I wasn't going to let a bunch of damn North Vietnamese communists ruin my strategic destiny by unleashing a three-pronged Easter Offensive against our troops and those of our South Vietnamese allies. On May eighth, 1972, I addressed the nation on television and said, "The communists have rejected all our peace initiatives and offered none of their own and they now threaten the liberty of seventeen million South Vietnamese as well as the lives of sixty thousand United States troops still in the region. Politically, I could certainly withdraw our remaining troops, for I did not put them there. I've already brought home a half million men while using restraint unparalleled in the annals of warfare. I could also continue negotiations, but the enemy would likely respond with more insults and contempt.

"Consequently, I have concluded that Hanoi must be denied the weapons and supplies it needs to continue the aggression. In coordination with our allies in South Vietnam, I have ordered the following measures that are being implemented as I'm speaking to you. All entrances to Vietnamese ports will be mined..."

From low altitudes our specialized aircraft, protected by other warplanes and warships, started releasing parachute-fitted mines to seal off Haiphong harbor which received eighty percent of the North's supplies arriving by sea. We also interdicted other points along the coast and attacked inland waterways and railroads.

"I know you took the right action, Dick, but what will the Russians do?" Pat asked after my speech. "Will they still let us visit?"

"I hope so. They surely understand that strategic arms talks are infinitely more important than what happens in the civil war of a primitive nation."

I didn't ask General Secretary Leonid Brezhnev if his invitation still applied. He'd have assumed I was overanxious and weak. I waited and worried I might lose this seminal chance. That would be a loss for mankind but, at last, I got word Brezhnev wanted to see us. Pat and I and Henry Kissinger and our aides would go to Moscow on May twenty-second. When I walked down the steps from Air Force One,

I was proud to be accompanied by my stylish wife, who on this trip often wore a long light blue coat.

The first few days I didn't have time for much sightseeing and instead spent many hours negotiating with Brezhnev. His interpreter provided translation.

"Our nations must avoid a direct confrontation," I said. "The casualties would be unimaginable."

"Mr. President, the Soviet Union understands death and destruction better than any nation," Brezhnev said. "More than twenty million of us died during World War II. Far more than that were wounded. Thousands of our cities, towns, and villages were destroyed. The war was fought on our soil. The United States fought heroically, on the soil of other people. That would not be the case in a nuclear war."

"You're correct, Mr. Secretary," I said, looking at Dr. Henry Kissinger and Foreign Minister Andrei Gromyko and their staffs. "That's why these gentlemen have spent three years working on the details of an agreement that can, and I believe will, save the world."

Brezhnev stood at least two inches shorter than I but was built like a bull and in that respect reminded me of Khrushchev. Despite our differences, I rather liked both men.

"We must have more missiles than you," Brezhnev told me.

"That's unreasonable. Everything should be equal."

"I thought you were seeking 'essential equivalence.'"

I nodded and said, "That's right."

"Your missiles, for the time being, can carry more nuclear warheads than ours. We therefore need more missiles. In earlier negotiations, our staffs tentatively agreed on this principle."

"What are your final projections for the Strategic Arms Limitations Talks?" I asked.

"We want about one thousand four hundred intercontinental ballistic missiles. You could deliver a comparable number of nuclear warheads with a thousand ICBMs."

I maintained a poker face and asked, "What about sea-launched ballistic missiles?"

"We need nine hundred fifty SLBMs. You could deter us with six hundred."

I shook my head and said, "No, Mr. Secretary, my military experts wouldn't accept less than seven hundred or so."

We took a break. I talked to Kissinger and our advisers. Brezhnev huddled with Gromyko and their advisers. Our groups ate lunch separately and a few hours after returning we shook hands on the essential details.

"Now," said Brezhnev, "we must make sure our respective missiles could get through and deter any threat. Our military and diplomatic experts agree that one hundred ABMs in each of two locations would not be destabilizing."

I felt like celebrating but remained seated and said, "Mr. Secretary, I'm prepared to sign the SALT and ABM treaties as soon as the official versions can be finalized."

"Let's do it May twenty-sixth, 1972."

On a long and lovely white table, backed by three dozen men in fine black, blue, and gray suits, Leonid Brezhnev and I signed the two historic treaties, and everyone rejoiced that we had just made the world significantly less dangerous. When we got home, I felt Kissinger and I deserved a tickertape parade. We settled for the love of a grateful nation.

Three weeks later, my chief of staff, H.R. Haldeman, entered the Oval Office.

"You look worried, Bob," I said. "What's the matter?"

"It's this story in the Washington Post. Some of our guys were arrested last night."

"Who?"

"The Plumbers investigative team we put together after Kent State a couple of years ago."

"What did they do?"

"Police captured them after they broke into the office of the Democratic National Committee in the Watergate Hotel."

Holding out my hand, I said, "Give me that newspaper… The Post says, 'The five men were accused of attempted burglary as well as telephone and other communications eavesdropping. Police found lock-picks and door jimmies, more than two thousand dollars in cash, a short-wave receiver to pick up police calls, rolls of unexposed films, two cameras, and three pen-sized tear gas guns.'

"What the hell's going on, Bob?"

He said, "I think The Plumbers believed they were acting in your interest."

I slammed the paper on my desk. "I just opened the world to China and made peace with Russia. Why the hell would I need some half-assed operation?"

"I agree, Mr. President."

"Is there any way this can somehow, erroneously, be connected to the White House?" I asked.

"Howard Hunt thinks he might've given his White House phone number to at least of the burglars."

"How the hell does a former CIA officer blunder like that?"

Haldeman didn't answer.

"Get the hell out," I said.

That night in our family quarters, Pat asked, "Dick, what's wrong?"

"Nothing. I'm just having a few drinks."

"Don't worry. George McGovern won't stand a chance."

I handed her the newspaper and said, "I'm not worried about him. It's this damn article."

She read it and said, "That doesn't have anything to do with you, does it?"

"Don't insult me."

During the campaign McGovern often talked about Watergate, what little he knew, and sometimes compared me to Hitler, but few people listened and not many voted for a man who wanted to make America weak. In November I won every state but one, capturing sixty percent of the popular vote, and raised both hands to flash victory signs.

In December I ordered Operation Linebacker, the largest bombing offensive of the war, to compel the communists to negotiate in good faith, and in January 1973 we signed "An Agreement Ending the War and Restoring Peace in Vietnam" with North Vietnam, South Vietnam, and the Viet Cong, and the following month our prisoners of war started coming home. Most of those soldiers didn't dwell on charges by the liberal media that my bombing Cambodia might have killed a hundred thousand people or that the Johnson and Nixon administrations and Congress may have been responsible for two million deaths in Vietnam and Southeast Asia. I didn't start the war. I ended it and brought peace with honor.

"I hate looking at the newspapers," Pat told me that March in our White House residence.

I squeezed her hand and said, "Don't pay any attention. This nonsense will soon be forgotten. People are happy I'm bringing home the last of our combat troops and abolishing the draft."

Thank God the foreign war was ending. I had more dangerous enemies at home.

In the Oval Office, John Dean, my White House counsel, told me, "The Watergate burglars, as well as Howard Hunt, are demanding more than a million dollars to pay for their legal and living expenses."

"We've already paid a lot," I said. "But I can get more. Tell them to relax."

"They say they can't continue the coverup much longer," said Dean.

I had trusted some bad people like James McCord, another ex-CIA agent, who became chief of security for fundraising in my final campaign. Now, he and a few others were convicted of burglary, wiretapping, and conspiracy. And Judge John Sirica, notorious for issuing long sentences, read aloud McCord's cowardly appeal for leniency: "The White House knew about and approved of the Watergate break-in... There was political pressure applied to the defendants to plead guilty and remain silent... Perjury occurred during the trial..."

On April thirtieth, Bob Haldeman resigned, at my insistence, and

I fired devious John Dean for telling the Senate Watergate Committee that I'd ordered a coverup since last fall. It was time to speak to the American people who that evening heard me say, "I want you... to know that throughout this process justice will be pursued fairly and vigorously... The presidency is a sacred office, and I intend to be worthy of that trust."

I sensed I still had broad support on May twenty-fourth when Pat and I hosted a huge party at the White House for POWs I'd recently liberated from Vietnam. They would've voted for Nixon that night, I assure you. I knew I also had the support of General Secretary Leonid Brezhnev who visited the following month and joined me in a pledge to prevent nuclear war. What's more important, saving the planet or John Dean telling prosecutors we discussed Watergate more than thirty times?

I wasn't hiding anything and didn't mind that Archibald Cox was hired as a special prosecutor in this politically motivated investigation. No one should've cared that Cox and the nation learned I'd been recording my Oval Office conversations and phone calls for two years. President Kennedy did the same. So did President Johnson. I told Archibald Cox and the Watergate witch hunters, "These communications are historical, sensitive, and absolutely confidential..."

I couldn't get any relief without a few drinks in private. That didn't make me an alcoholic. I never drank during the day. I never drank when I had speeches or official meetings at night. I drank at home after work like millions of Americans.

And one night in our bedroom, I told Pat, "I hope to hell I don't wake up tomorrow."

"I won't let anything happen to you."

"I've at least got to resign."

"You can't quit," she said. "You've got to fight to prove you've been telling the truth. Our daughters feel the same way. You know that."

In the morning, Pat said, "It's time for you to address the people again."

I agreed. Average citizens had always loved me. Only the media and other enemies hated me, and I loathed them even more.

On August fifteenth, 1973, I told the silent majority, "These are cynical efforts to implicate the president personally. The facts are quite straightforward. I had no prior knowledge of the Watergate break-in. I neither know nor took part in any of the subsequent activities. That is the simple truth. I continued to ask my aides and always received the same answer — only the five burglars and two supervisors were involved in the coverup.

"Regarding the tapes, they simply cannot be turned over. Doing so would cause irreparable damage to our country. People would never feel comfortable talking to the president privately and frankly about essential matters."

In a just world I could have focused my energies on saving Israel from simultaneous invasions by Egyptian and Syrian forces and rushing enormous quantities of arms to our small and imperiled ally and then warning the Russians not to attack Israeli forces in the Sinai Peninsula where, propelled by my military aid, they had encircled an Egyptian army. Instead of letting me be a wartime president, Archibald Cox and his conspirators intensified efforts to seize my confidential tapes.

"Don't let them," Pat said.

"I should fire Archibald Cox, but I can't."

"You certainly can."

"I can't personally fire him. That's the job of Attorney General Elliot Richardson."

"Go and do it."

On October twentieth, 1973, a Saturday night, I went to the Oval Office and summoned Richardson and told him, "Cox is causing me serious problems."

"I guaranteed him I wouldn't interfere with his investigation."

"I want him out of the way."

"I won't go back on my word, Mr. President. Open up to the American people. Being so secretive hurts you."

"I may have to relieve you of your office."

"I'd resign rather than carry of this order," said Richardson."

"I accept your resignation, just give me something in writing. I'll talk to Ruckelshaus."

Deputy Attorney General William Ruckelshaus appeared in less than an hour, and I said, "I want Cox fired right away."

"I can't do that, Mr. President. I promised to let him investigate independently."

"Are you disobeying me?"

"Yes sir," he said.

"I want your letter of resignation on my desk by tomorrow morning."

"You shall have it."

Next, I summoned Solicitor General Robert Bork.

"You know why you're here."

"Yes, Mr. President," said Bork.

"Notify Cox at once."

"All right. But I may resign."

Bork performed his duty and kept his job. I feared I was losing mine as jackals in the press began calling my efforts to protect presidential privacy a Saturday Night Massacre. In little more than a week Congress moved to impeach me and hired another special prosecutor.

Soon thereafter, when my vice president, Spiro Agnew, resigned due to difficulties unrelated to Watergate, I selected Gerald Ford, the House Minority Leader, as his successor. The D.C. rumormongers tried to be clever: "We won't have to wait until 1976 to get a new president... I'll lay ten to one that Ford's in command within six months... I'll bet a hundred to one that Nixon's already forced Ford to pardon him..."

I wouldn't need a pardon. In November 1973 I told a group of newspaper managing editors and the nation that I wasn't a crook, I'd earned everything I owned, and had no idea why one of the tapes had an eighteen-minute gap. Ultimately, my longtime secretary Rose Mary Woods explained she'd accidentally caused the erasure.

The following April I clarified all investigative matters by releasing not the tapes but more than a thousand transcript pages. To save Congress time, my staff had deleted everything irrelevant to Watergate. The Supreme Court, including three justices I'd nominated during my first administration, voted unanimously that I had to turn over all the tapes, unedited.

"Don't worry, Dick," Pat said. "Let them have the tapes. They'll exonerate you."

"This is now more about saving the institution of the presidency from enemies of the state."

"But you will be exonerated, won't you?"

"I'm confident that I should be. But remember, Pat, they've many times investigated us, and they're still digging for more dirt about our private finances. I don't think anyone can forever withstand so much scrutiny."

"The girls and I still believe in you."

I retired to my den, built a fire, and relaxed as I examined my political achievements and felt secure as commander in chief. And in June 1974 I delivered another groundbreaking diplomatic achievement, promoting peace in the Middle East during visits to Israel, Egypt, Jordan, Syria, and Saudi Arabia. No other president had ventured there.

Surely, Americans outside Washington, D.C. cared more about my achievements than Watergate, but enemies intensified their investigations and dirty tricks, and on August seventh they released excerpts from conversations I'd had with Bob Haldeman on June twenty-third, 1972, six days after the Watergate story appeared, when Haldeman said, "(Director Patrick) Gray doesn't exactly know how to control (the FBI), and their investigation is now leading into some productive areas because they've been able to trace the money… The way to handle this now is… call Gray and just say, 'Stay the hell out of this…'"

"Um huh," I'd replied.

A few more unpleasant pages proved I'd learned about this bumbling criminal activity early on and should have started firing asses on the spot. All right, I'd tried to keep it quiet. But I hadn't planned or authorized the damn break-in. None of that mattered to the hordes who wanted Nixon's blood, and two senators and a representative marched into my Oval Office and said, "You have at most fifteen votes in the Senate, less than half what you'd need to survive the impeachment trial. You better resign soon."

"I'd like to thank you gentlemen for the candid assessment. Please show yourselves out."

The following day, Rose Mary Woods called me in the Oval Office and said, "Bob Haldeman again."

"I don't want to talk to him."

"I think he'll keep calling," she said.

"All right. I'll talk to him once."

"Mr. President," said Haldeman, "given my years of loyalty, I'm frankly disappointed you haven't taken my calls."

"You and the others talk too much."

"All we need is a pardon. It would take you two minutes. Otherwise, we're looking at a few years in prison."

"I'd be signing my historical obituary."

"Only if you pardoned everyone at once. You could do one or two at a time, starting with me."

I switched the phone to my other ear and said, "I'm not pardoning any of you."

"Mr. President, you've screwed up as much as anyone."

"I realize that now. But I didn't start it. You and a band of rouge former CIA and FBI agents did."

"We wouldn't have unless we thought you'd approve."

"Tell the others: no pardons."

"Except for yourself," Haldeman said.

I hung up.

Upstairs in our quarters, Pat, slender and silent, had been packing our furniture, clothes, and personal items, and I thought she was about to faint when I said, "Please sit down and rest."

"We've got to be out tomorrow," she said. "I don't know if I can survive two more speeches."

During my resignation address that night, August eighth, 1974, I stated, "I would have preferred to carry through to the finish whatever personal agony it would have involved, and my family unanimously urged me to do so. But the interest of the nation must always come before any personal considerations... I have never been a quitter. To leave office before my term is completed is abhorrent to every instinct in my body. But... I shall resign the presidency effective at noon tomorrow."

Afterward, in our private quarters, a photographer asked Pat and me to stand in the middle with Tricia and her husband Edward Cox on one side and Julie and David Eisenhower on the other.

"Everybody smile," he said.

We smiled tightly the first several times but then got it right and looked happy like a family together at home. We stayed up late, Pat and the kids packing while I worked on my farewell speech to the White House staff.

Standing at the door to my study, Pat said, "Dick, you aren't going to let them film this one, are you?"

"I sure am, and history will thank me."

The following day our family walked into the East Room and joined hundreds of advisers, aides, cooks, maids, and others. I thanked them for always having a smile for me when I was down and said I was proud of them and proud that "no man or no woman ever profited at the public expense or the public till...Mistakes, yes. But for personal gain, never. You did what you believed in. Sometimes right, sometimes wrong...I only wish that I were a wealthy man...and if I were, I would like to recompense you for the sacrifices that all of you have made to serve in government. But you are getting something in government service that is far more important than money. It is a cause bigger than yourself..."

Outside the White House, walking through a cordon to the

helicopter, I urged myself: you've gotta do it. You know you do. No one'll be expecting it. Everyone's so solemn and uncomfortable. They feel for you. That's more important than all the applause, more vital than any political victory. So, you really must do it. When you finish climbing the stairs to the helicopter door, turn. That's it. Turn and thrust your arms in the air and flash your legendary victory signs with both hands. Smile and flash those signs with vigor because that's what people will remember.

Fidel Forever

Some say I'm a hick from a sugar plantation and loco because on a dare I rammed my bicycle into a prep school wall and knocked myself unconscious. They think I'm a hotheaded and dangerous young man who may someday kill people and might already have as a politically obsessed law student at Havana University. Don't listen to lies planted by the cretinous Fulgencio Batista. Perhaps some of my classmates are trying to help the dictator. Don't bother with them, either. They'll never be revolutionaries. I know I will. I'm brilliant. And I'm a big tough dynamic guy. No one denies that. Women love me. Men line up to follow. I'm like a movie star.

I'm only twenty-six but ready to take over Cuba and destroy the murderous Batista regime and evict all imperialists from my island. I would have proceeded democratically. I was running for a minor office in 1952 but before the election Batista wrapped his dark hand around Cuba. Now I'm going to remove it. I know where to start. I'm going after Moncada Barracks, the second largest military installation in the country.

I've been planning for a year, gathering supporters and stockpiling shotguns and .22 rifles. I know when to strike – early morning July twenty-sixth, 1953. The Carnival in Santiago de Cuba will end late the night before and soldiers at Moncada Barracks are likely to be drunk or hungover or asleep. Few will be at their posts. And why would those young men fight to support Batista? I'll convince them to join us and yield their weapons and radio transmitter, and we'll broadcast that the revolution has begun and Batista's being overthrown.

On July twenty-fourth my comrades and I board two buses in Havana. After riding several hundred miles to Cuba's southeast, we gather at a farm twenty miles from Moncada Barracks and put on stolen army uniforms and then grind into a convoy of two dozen cars. Looking like high-ranking officers, we plan to bluff our way in.

The final part of the drive is very dark, and I worry a little. Some people aren't keeping up. Where's the car with our biggest weapons? Maybe we won't need them. My plan is impeccable. It better be. We have less than a hundred men to attack five or ten times that. By five a.m. we're close to Moncada Barracks. Some of our cars are rolling through the gateway when a patrol confronts us outside the walls. I don't wait, I jump out firing, and they fire back. Other comrades dash from their cars, clutching old rifles, and we capture a few soldiers. But others are shooting at us from doorways and barracks windows, shredding us while our bullets hit yellow walls.

There's no choice but to retreat through the dark, evading enemy soldiers, and break up as we run several hours into the Sierra Maestra mountains. Don't tell me I should stay and get shot. I must live for the revolution. I did everything possible and couldn't have prevented a dozen or more comrades being killed on the spot. Most of the others were captured and many tortured to death. This message is relayed to me: "Give up, and we'll let you live. We won't even torture you, Fidel. We won't rip out your eyes and present them to a relative, as we've just done with a traitorous brother and sister. We'll give you a fair trial."

I doubt it'll be fair, but I believe there'll at least be a trial. My family has a large sugar plantation and my elegant wife, Mirta, is even wealthier. She uses contacts with Catholic priests who convince family acquaintance Batista to spare me. Back in Havana student leaders call me irresponsible and accuse me of cowardice. They're jealous. They've achieved nothing and never will. I'm the one becoming famous.

At my trial in Santiago de Cuba, I declare, "I am the most abused client and lawyer in history and haven't been permitted to read the indictment. As the accused, I've been locked into solitary confinement and held incommunicado. This is of course a violation of every human and legal right... The right of rebellion against tyranny has been recognized from the most ancient times to the present day by men of all creeds, ideas, and doctrines. Let us remember the most beautiful part of the Declaration of Independence, that all men are created equal and endowed by their Creator with certain inalienable rights among which are life, liberty, and the pursuit of happiness... Whenever any form of government becomes destructive of these ends, it is the right of the people to alter or abolish it and institute a new government...

"Go ahead. Send me to prison so that I can share the fate of my comrades. It is understandable that honest men should be dead or in prison in a republic where the president is a criminal and a thief. If you choose, condemn me. It does not matter. History will absolve me."

In fact, I know that I will forge history. And prison helps. What a wonderful school it is. I read all the time. Marx and Lenin are my favorites. I also devour works by Dostoevsky, Freud, Hugo, and a book by our great revolutionary Jose Martí, and a volume about United States history, and stacks of others. I receive many books from Natalia Revuelta, the beautiful wife of a doctor she stopped caring for the moment she met me and soon offered the key to her house in Havana. Now we write each other exquisite letters. She sends me sand from a beach and photos of folk dancers, and she says, "You were there. I saw you dancing."

"You are a special type of honey that never satiates," I reply. "I ask you now to stop using the typewriter and write longhand. I love your handwriting, so delicate, feminine, unmistakable...Write to me, for I cannot endure without your letters."

Under Batista a man cannot maintain private correspondence. His reactionary prison director sends one of my letters for Natalia to my wife, Mirta, and a letter for Mirta to Natalia. My special friend understands. My wife does not. She files for divorce and takes our child, Fidelito, to Mexico City. I write her, "I'll get my son back even if the earth should be destroyed in the process."

I'm not going to be in prison forever. I'm not even going to be here the official fifteen years. Batista is under pressure to release me. He must do something besides repress and murder. He lifts press censorship and in 1955 amnesties me and my brother Raúl and other comrades. I rush to see Natalia. Our time together is precious, and two months later, as I leave her and my homeland for exile in Mexico City, she's carrying my child.

The Mexican capital for many years has been a crucible of revolutionary activity and discourse. Trotsky lived in exile and was murdered here. Diego Rivera still here paints socialist masterpieces. In the elegant Chapultepec neighborhood, I meet a dashing and politically committed Argentine. His name is Ché Guevara.

"I hear you're quite a revolutionary," I tell him.

"Not yet," he says. "In Guatemala I simply denounced the United States for backing the United Fruit Company at the expense of poor Guatemalans."

"Are you ready to fight imperialists and liberate the people they oppress?"

"Sí, I'm committed to that cause for life."

"Then I want you to join my movement."

Ché shakes my hand and embraces me.

With about eighty comrades Raúl, Ché, and I sail on the yacht Granma. This time we're going to liberate Cuba. We'll strike right after landing. We would have, but instead we're running. Batista's soldiers have sighted our ship and they're shooting and capturing us but they don't get me. I'm hiding in a sugarcane field. Three days later I walk into the Sierra Maestra mountains. Raúl and Ché also make it. We have nineteen hungry men growing beards in harsh terrain, yet I know I'll soon take over. I am, after all, fighting a fool. Can you fathom why Batista didn't kill me immediately after my attack on Moncada Barracks? Or after my trial? Or when I was in prison? Why didn't he immediately pursue me in the mountains? What an unmitigated buffoon. Do you think I'd let anyone loose under comparable circumstances?

In the Sierra Maestra we are happy. We're remaking the world. And the world wants to meet me. The New York Times sends legendary correspondent Herbert Matthews to write a three-part piece for the front page. He understands what I tell him in English I learned during my extended 1948 honeymoon in New York City. I don't tell Matthews that my wealthy father had given me money to buy a Lincoln Continental.

He doesn't need that. He reports the essence, "Castro is quite a man, a powerful six-footer with olive skin and strong ideas about liberty, democracy, and social justice."

Next, CBS sends a documentary crew to whom I explain, "Batista can't defeat us or even decide whether to claim I'm dead or alive or insignificant. He can only lie that his soldiers are dying because of accidents in the Sierra Maestra."

Everyone knows his regime is itself a series of fatal errors. We must prepare for the transition. When opposition leaders from other parties come to me in the mountains, we prepare the Manifesto of the Sierra Maestra proclaiming that soon Cuba will be a democratic republic and offer free elections. These are great ideals and must not be undermined by those either incompetent or disobedient. Raúl and Ché always follow orders. When others don't, I stand over them, cursing, threatening, and humiliating. This I do only for the revolution and the people of Cuba whose suffering must end.

In 1958 Batista launches Summer Operation with ten thousand troops who surround us in the Sierra Maestra. He should have shot them himself. We do so for him. They're dispirited and disoriented in strange and inhospitable terrain and never know where we're next going to strike. Every time we kill one, at least five desert, prompting the opportunistic North Americans to withdraw military support for Batista. Bad news for the cretin but immaterial to me, and I vow, "Once this struggle is over, I'll begin the real struggle of my life, the fight against the United States."

We leave the Sierra Maestra and advance west and south across Cuba, liberating cities and towns, blowing up trains, and driving hot stakes into the frozen heart of the Batista regime. On December thirty-first, 1958, the cretin flees with hundreds of millions of dollars. Two days later my portion of the rebel army starts marching six hundred miles from Santiago de Cuba to Havana. Everywhere along the way I embrace enraptured people as radio microphones and television cameras carry my words and images across Cuba. I'm already a hero.

Arriving in Havana I experience an effusion of love, and respond by quickly trying, convicting, and executing hundreds of Batista's traitors who've inflicted so much pain. I'm cleansing the nation to start the real revolution. In February 1959, as stipulated in the Manifesto of the Sierra Maestra, an interim government is established and I, inevitably, am named prime minister.

In April I go to the United States and am welcomed as a celebrity and appear on Meet the Press to deny Yanqui accusations that Ché and my brother Raúl and others close to me are communists. How can people claim that? I've heard no such thing. I also meet Vice President Richard Nixon, an unsavory fellow who's made his career by inciting anti-communist hysteria. He presumes to tell me, "You need to hold elections as soon as possible."

"Cubans don't want elections," I reply. "In the past they've produced bad government."

Our people want land. In May, we institute the Agrarian Reform Law. And the first land confiscated is quite correctly my family's plantation, Las Manacas.

"Fidel, I'll shoot you or anyone else who tries to take my property," says my mother.

"This is for the good of all Cubans and an honor for you to be in the vanguard," I tell her, and she relents.

We then collectivize other farms and expropriate property held by rich Cubans and others. Everyone must embrace the revolution. We're at war, not so much with remnants of the dead Batista regime but with the United States. President Eisenhower promptly slashes our sugar import quota by seven hundred thousand tons. I counter by nationalizing a billion dollars of U.S. property and stating, "We must extirpate every root of imperialism. The Yanquis will never treat us as adult human beings. Last century they codified, in the Platt Amendment, their 'right' to intervene in Cuba whenever they pleased. And now they refuse to refine the oil we just agreed to purchase from our socialist brothers in the Soviet Union."

Naturally, I expropriate those refineries on Cuban soil, and the petulant Yanquis sever diplomatic relations. This is great news, for it motivates Premier Nikita Khrushchev and his comrades to offer enormous military and economic aid. I further alarm the Eisenhower administration when I fly to New York in September 1960 and, before a capacity audience, tell the United Nations General Assembly, "I was degraded and humiliated when denied access to several hotels and then evicted from one that finally admitted me. Only a Negro hotel in Harlem would take us."

"The Cuban delegation is staying in a brothel," the U.S. soon responds.

And I counter, "They think Cuba is still an American colony, one where the imperialists, until I came to power, owned public utilities, a major portion of banking and importing businesses, the oil refineries, and the best land including most of the sugar production. They think submissive Cubans will permit U.S.-produced planes to fly over our emerging nation, dropping pamphlets on Havana and incendiary bombs on sugarcane fields. These are acts of war by an arrogant bully."

Privately, I don't see how a Democratic victory in November will change imperialistic U.S. attitudes about Cuba. Senator John F. Kennedy spends much of his campaign trying to be tougher on communism than Nixon. And Kennedy plans to increase defense spending. His running mate, Senator Lyndon Baines Johnson, is just as belligerent, stating, "When we're in power, I'm gonna first take that Castro fellow and wash him. And then shave him. And then spank him."

I wonder if Lyndon Johnson would've spanked me in the Sierra Maestra. Believe me, no one is going to degrade Fidel Castro. I'm building a powerful and now well-equipped armed forces and security apparatus to ensure my survival and thus that of the revolution. Millions of Cubans often rush to hear my vital five-hour speeches about external threats. Naturally, many stunning young women are enamored. I understand their feelings and privately assist them because they've helped me and therefore their country. I give them houses and let them live there quietly and wait for my visits. I need companionship. What I had with Natalia Revuelta has passed, and my visits to her and our unstable little daughter are simply not going to continue. I'm sorry her husband has divorced her and left the country with their biological daughter, but Naty knows she contributed to the revolution, and I will always help her.

The entire world needs my heroic assistance. Cuba is the focal point of international revolution and the most important bastion against imperialism. This terrifies the Yanquis, and they continue and then intensify the economic aggression of the previous administration. They don't know how to deal with Latin American countries as equals. They only understand protecting their investments by ordering reactionary puppet armies, in places like Nicaragua and Guatemala, to suppress the people. They've also used direct military aggression more times than I have space to list. Is there any reason to think they won't attack Cuba?

"The Kennedy administration daily makes aggressive statements and is forming a council of traitors in exile," I explain to reporters. "Meanwhile, the U.S. press writes that counterrevolutionaries might strike us in many areas to establish networks for further operations. Or the Yanquis might land their whole force in one place and try to secure territory from which they can establish a provisional government and receive supplies and reinforcements and bomb us. We are on alert, prepared for any incursion, and confident of victory."

Radio warnings and antiaircraft fire reveal that one of our airfields is being bombed on April fifteenth, 1961. We quickly alert our pilots at several other bases to take off but learn they're already under attack. Imperialists often destroy unprepared victims on the ground, but our few planes and fewer pilots are dispersed and damage is minimal and we force treasonous Cuban attackers to flee back to Miami. On our domestic front, we swiftly arrest tens of thousands of counterrevolutionary swine who will die if this dastardly attack succeeds.

Two days later Yanqui-equipped Cuban backstabbers signal the primary attack, parachuting into the Bay of Pigs, and we unleash all our soldiers and planes and ships and fight without cease. We lose many men but kill far more invaders and take four hundred fifty prisoners. Rather than accept the will of our people, U.S. politicians threaten, "We must directly intervene in Cuba and overthrow the communists."

"How calmly they ignore international law and threaten us with more intervention," I respond. "And they talk as if it were so easy… They should instead consider the sorrow that military aggression causes – all to restore their privileges here. What need was there to bring this bloodshed to our country? Let the Yanquis understand: we'd rather die than live under their yoke."

Our brave Soviet ally, Nikita Khrushchev, secretly offers to place nuclear missiles in Cuba. At first, I hesitate, knowing the United States will find out, but soon realize this is an extraordinary opportunity and urge Khrushchev to begin the necessary shipping and building. Isn't this extraordinary? A man who a few years ago hid in the mountains with a handful of exhausted comrades will soon be armed with the ultimate weapons. Inevitably, on October twenty-second, 1962, President Kennedy announces on radio and television that his country has discovered ballistic missile bases in Cuba, and he orders a naval blockade around the island. He also threatens that any missiles fired from Cuba will result in a full retaliatory response upon the Soviet Union.

I know the Yanquis will soon attack. They're amassing at least two hundred thousand invasion soldiers in the southeast of their country. On October twenty-seventh we shoot down a U-2 spy plane, and I write Khrushchev, urging him to be ready to unleash his missiles the moment the United States invades. Millions of North Americans should die if their country destroys Cuba and the Soviet Union. At least our heroic sacrifice would be for the glory of international socialism.

Later that day a cable arrives. It isn't from Khrushchev. It's a news cable, one anyone could've written. The announcement appalls me: the Russians are withdrawing their missiles.

"Khrushchev is a coward and a bastard and a son of a bitch," I scream, and shatter a mirror in my office as assistants shrink. "He's just another big power bully using Cuba to control the North Americans in Europe. Granted, he extracted a promise from Kennedy that the United States won't invade Cuba. But what does that mean? I don't believe it."

I return to my guerilla camp in the Sierra Maestra to mourn the death of the revolution. What a horrible outcome, not having nuclear weapons. How can I survive? I decide to forgive Khrushchev but won't trust him as much. Really, who else is there? After he's ousted in 1964, I work with his successors. They're quite generous, letting us trade our sugar at inflated prices for their oil at deflated levels. They also give me arms and help strengthen my security state. My revolution will survive as long as I remain vigilant. I simply have to know what everyone's doing and thinking and be prepared to stifle all criticism and suppress every opponent. My prisons are full, and enemies claim tens of thousands of political prisoners are being tortured and executed. How do they know? They don't. They're guessing, and I'm not counting.

Ours is a humane revolution attracting young people from all over the world. They come to Cuba to learn and train and prepare to fight the enemy of everyone. We can't hit him directly, so we strike his interests all over the world. In that regard I sometimes consult Ché Guevara, my dear and dynamic comrade who, rifle in hand, had helped me liberate Cuba, and now supervises our central bank. I'm concerned about Che's performance in the latter assignment and summon him to a secret location near Havana and tell him, "Don't worry. I'm not angry. You aren't entirely responsible for our staggering economy. The imperialists are also to blame. So, you shouldn't continually criticize the Russians in public. That's bad policy. And you shouldn't denounce our socialist brothers for insisting we focus our economy on sugar production. Nor should you declare, 'The socialist countries are, in a way, accomplices of imperialist exploitation.'"

"I speak for myself, Fidel," he says.

"On the contrary, I speak for you and everyone else in Cuba."

"I'm going to continue saying what I believe. That's the only way to keep the revolution pure."

I frown at Ché before telling him, "I don't want to arrest you. That would be embarrassing. I've therefore decided what you must do is leave administration and pursue your real work, eternal revolution outside Cuba. The freedom-seeking people of the Congo need you. Go there and help them."

I want to help him succeed in the Congo in 1965. It isn't his fault the imperialists win there. I'm thankful Ché barely escapes. Through government channels he sends word he wants to come home. I reply with a confidential message that my agent delivers in a strong voice, "Cuba's no longer your home and never really was. You can visit but only after completely disguising yourself so your wife will barely recognize you and your young children will think they're meeting a family friend."

At our brief reunion, I tell him, "Don't be disheartened. You'll find another country. We both understand that Cuba will forever have but one comandante en jefe. Please behave during your visit here. My agents will always be nearby, protecting you and the revolution."

"You're most considerate," he says.

Ché shrewdly chooses to next fight in Bolivia, which has a political party that will support him. So will people in the countryside. He and his one hundred twenty guerillas start off so well. He's finally going to overcome failure and become a hero again. Then he's betrayed. The Bolivian Communist Party declines to join him and so do the very people he came to help. High in the eastern Andes he's being hunted by specially trained agents of the imperialists. I can't do anything. It's a lie I'm receiving radio messages from him or those close to him. It's a lie I can send help from La Paz or Paraguay. I can do nothing but mourn in October 1967 when my special comrade is captured and shot and photographed on a stone slab.

I can't save the earthly Ché, but I create a far greater man, a super revolutionary whose heroic face will forever gaze from massive walls and millions of photos and books and posters and T-shirts and will in fact shine in the hearts and minds of revolutionaries the world over. I will continue his work and strike wherever there is upheaval. I will strike for the people. I will strike in the spirit of Ché.

The Russians tell me to quit agitating so much. I ignore them and they then tell me to stop altogether or they'll give the North Americans an opening in Cuba. They claim I'm ruining their arms control efforts. Then they learn who their most important ally is. In 1968 they invade Czechoslovakia and enrage much of the world. Like the ultimate freedom fighter, I step before the world and announce, "Czech counterrevolutionaries were moving Czechoslovakia toward capitalism and into the arms of imperialists... Leaders of the rebellion are agents of West Germany and fascist reactionary rabble."

That proclamation earns more loans and oil for my people. Do I believe everything I say? I don't know and neither does anyone else.

I do understand it's best to ignore U.S. offers of improved relations and instead invade Angola and Namibia to fight South African agents of apartheid in 1975, and join Ethiopia in the Ogaden War against Somalia in 1977, and help the Sandinistas oust the rotten Somoza dynasty from Nicaragua in 1979, and I say not a word against the Soviet invasion of Afghanistan. As a result of shrewd foreign policy, my status and control at home become ever more absolute. A new generation has now seen only me as their leader. They are most fortunate, never having to pay for health care or education. And in gratitude they should ignore jokes that my real name is "Mister There Will Be." They must be patient and realize better days are coming.

I know how to overcome any contingency, even the 1991 collapse of the Soviet Union. I don't panic, I remember the good things Stalin did and know I won't be an idiot like Gorbachev and allow – much less promote – "openness and reforms." Those are threats to my socialist principles and still get you a one-way ride to prison or worse. Rather than change, I give seven-hour speeches and fall off a stage and shatter my knee in 2004 but recover rapidly and publicly stand in the presence of my socialist brothers.

I also proclaim that Cuba has twice as many doctors per capita as any other nation and the best health care of all and eighty-five percent of Cubans own their homes and others pay only ten percent of their salaries for rent. I remind everyone, "My actions in Angola and Namibia now prove I sped up the end of apartheid by twenty to twenty-five years."

I remain an infallible and mysterious leader and pretend I'm not really married even though I am and have five sons with Dalia Soto Del Valle. In fact, I have another son by a woman now long dead, and all seven – including Fidelito – adore me. Only my daughter by Naty Revuelta is critical, and she has an eating disorder and four divorces and capitalist motives to attack me. But you can't read that in Cuba. You can read only propaganda releases and texts of my speeches and other state-approved material. That's all you've needed for a half century, and that's all you'll ever need. Talk to the people in the streets of Havana. Most will tell you, "Democracy sounds okay but isn't necessary in Cuba. No one could do as well as Fidel."

Sources

Robert Walker – *Star-Crossed* by Beverly Linet; *Bataan; Since You Went Away; Thirty Seconds Over Tokyo; Vengeance Valley; Strangers on a Train;* "Farley Granger Talks about Robert Walker" and *Strangers on a Train*, YouTube March 2011; "Patricia Hitchcock Talks about *Strangers on a Train,*" YouTube March 2016.

Power Couple – *The Bennetts: An Acting Family* by Brian Kellow; *Trade Winds; Foreign Correspondent; The House Across the Bay; Man Hunt; The Woman in the Window; Scarlet Street; Father's Little Dividend; Riot in Cell Block 11; Highway Dragnet.*

The Educator – Bakersfield.com and local network television affiliates posted four years of insightful online reports and videos about the Vincent Brothers investigation and trial. I'd also like to commend a real estate agent for letting me into the house of the murder victims and numerous people in the community who shared their feelings about an appalling crime.

Alternative Interrogation – *I'll Be Gone in the Dark* by Michelle McNamara; I lived in Sacramento during the East Area Rapist's rampages there in the late 1970s and read hundreds of articles about the then-unknown assailant. Almost everyone in the city was appalled and often discussed their feelings about the crisis. Those experiences prompted me to seek psychic revenge during a tough but not brutal imaginary interrogation of Joe DeAngelo, who escaped justice more than forty years.

The Slugger – *The Age of Anxiety, McCarthyism to Terrorism* by Haynes Johnson; Reexamining the Life and Legacy of America's Most Hated Senator by Arthur Herman in the Free Press, 1999; Joseph McCarthy, Wikipedia.

Nixon Responds – *Pat Nixon: The Untold Story* by Julie Nixon-Eisenhower; The Checkers Speech, 1952; White House Farewell Speech of 1974; *The Powers That Be* by David Halberstam; Excerpt from *Tricky Dick and the Pink Lady* by Greg Mitchell

Fidel Forever – Fidel Castro's testimony at his 1953 treason trial; *The Best and the Brightest* by David Halberstam; *Khrushchev Remembers* by Nikita Khrushchev; *Ché Guevara* by Jon Lee Anderson; "History Will Absolve Me," Castro Internet Archive; "First Shots in a Revolution," Epinions.com; "Castro's Failed Coup at the Moncada Barracks," PBS. org; "The Problem of Cuba and its Revolutionary Policy," Castro Internet Archive; "We Must Defend Our Country," Castro Internet Archive; "Cuba's Achievements and America's Wars," Castro Internet Archive; "Blaming Stalin for Everything would be Historical Simplism," Castro Internet Archive "A '50s Affair: Fidel and Naty," U.S. News & World Report; "Castro's Family," The Miami Herald; "Fulgencio Batista," PBS.org; "Ché Guevara," PBS.org; "Cuban Missile Crisis," Encarta.msn.com; "Fidel Castro," American Experience PBS.org; "Fidel Castro," Wikipedia.org.

About the Author

George Thomas Clark has written numerous books including *Hitler Here*, a biographical novel, *They Make Movies*, a collection of creative stories about actors and actresses, *Paint it Blue*, stories about painters, *Autobiography of George Thomas Clark*, highlights from his life, *The Bold Investor*, a short story collection, *Where Will We Sleep*, portraits of people mired in prostitution, human trafficking, and poverty, *Basketball and Football*, and four books of political satire.

If you enjoyed any of the author's books, please leave a review.

Visit the George Thomas Clark page on Amazon.com or on Barnes & Noble, Apple Books, Kobo Books, and other easily-accessed digital stores and websites that focus on books.